Atlas of Highland Land Mammals

Edited
by
Ro Scott

Highland
Biological
Recording
Group

Published in 2011 by the
Highland Biological Recording Group

ISBN 978-0-9552211-3-2

Printed on recycled paper by
Big Sky, 305 The Park, Findhorn, IV36 3TE
01309 691641

Front cover photo: Pine marten © James A Moore
www.jamesamoore.co.uk

Contents

		Page
Introduction		3
Highland mammal history		5
Acknowledgements		6
Number of records per species		7
Map of Atlas coverage		Ʊ
Explanation of the Species Accounts and Maps		9
Locations of the smaller islands mentioned in the text		10
The species accounts and maps		
Rodents:	Red squirrel and grey squirrel by Ro Scott	11
	Bank vole by Ro Scott	15
	Field vole by Ian Evans	18
	Water vole by Becks Denny	21
	Wood mouse by Ro Scott	25
	House mouse by Ro Scott	28
	Common rat by Ro Scott	31
Lagomorphs:	Rabbit by Ray Collier	34
	Brown hare by Ray Collier	37
	Mountain hare by Ray Collier	40
Insectivores:	Hedgehog by Ro Scott	43
	Mole by Ro Scott	46
	Common shrew by Ro Scott	49
	Pygmy shrew by Ro Scott	52
	Water shrew by Ro Scott	55
Bats:	Introduction by David Patterson & Lyn Wells	58
	Daubenton's bat by David Patterson & Lyn Wells	59
	Natterer's bat by Shirley Pottie	62
	Noctule by Shirley Pottie	64
	Common pipistrelle by David Patterson & Lyn Wells	66
	Soprano pipistrelle by David Patterson & Lyn Wells	70
	Brown long-eared bat by David Patterson & Lyn Wells	74
Colour plates I - IV		
Carnivores:	Wildcat and feral cat by Ro Scott	78
	Fox by Ro Scott	82
	Badger by Roger Cottis	85
	Otter by Grace Yoxon & Paul Yoxon	88
	Pine marten by Roger Cottis	92
	Stoat by Ro Scott	95
	Weasel by Ro Scott	99
	Polecat and feral ferret by Ro Scott	102
	American mink by Ro Scott	105
Seals:	Common seal by Ro Scott	108
	Grey seal by Ro Scott	111
Ungulates:	Wild boar by Ro Scott	114

Red deer by Ray Collier 116
Sika by Ray Collier 120
Roe deer by Ray Collier 123
Feral goat by Ray Collier 126
Escapes, semi-domesticated, vagrants and unconfirmed 129
References 131
Further reading 137
Useful organisations and websites 139
Index of species 140

Why not join HBRG?

Membership of the Highland Biological Recording Group is open to anyone, resident or visitor, with an interest in recording any aspect of Highland natural history. We hold two indoor meetings per year, in spring and autumn, and publish one issue of our magazine 'The Highland Naturalist'. In summer we organise a series of field meetings to record particular species groups or localities. The annual subscription is currently £6. Find out more from our website www.hbrg.org.uk or contact the treasurer/membership secretary: treasurer@hbrg.org.uk

Highland
Biological
Recording
Group

Introduction

Background This Atlas represents the results of mammal recording by members of the Highland Biological Recording Group (HBRG), local Mammal Society members, and many other individuals over the 12-year period 1999-2010. HBRG had previously carried out several mammal surveys (bats 1987; otter/mink 1988; pine marten 1989; feral goat 1990; hedgehog and red squirrel, 1991; brown hare and mountain hare 1992; stoat and weasel 1996; small mammals in owl pellets and hedgehog roadkill 1997). Records from these surveys are included here. The Mammal Atlas started as a five-year project, but we quickly realised that to get reasonable coverage for a group as diverse as mammals over an area the size of Highland (one third of the land mass of Scotland) would need a much longer time. Looking at the final maps, there is still a considerable amount of recording to be done, particularly in the more remote areas away from the main roads and settlements. We hope that publishing this Atlas will act a stimulus to such work. The last published mammal atlas covering Highland was the national 'Atlas of Mammals in Britain' published by the Institute of Terrestrial Ecology (now the Centre for Ecology and Hydrology) in 1993 (Arnold, 1993). We have used this as our baseline for comparing real or apparent distributional changes.

What is included This Atlas covers only the terrestrial mammals (including the airborne bats and amphibious seals). The truly marine whales, dolphins and porpoises are not included because they require different methods of recording, and there are several specialised groups dedicated to their study.

Our recording area The HBRG recording area is the administrative area covered by the Highland Council. This equates to the former local authority Districts of Caithness, Sutherland, Ross & Cromarty, Inverness & Nairn, Skye & Lochalsh, Badenoch & Strathspey and Lochaber. This area is given as 'Highland' with a capital letter in the text, whereas the geographical term 'the highlands' (not capitalised), means mainland Scotland north of the Highland Boundary Fault. The locations of the smaller islands mentioned in the text are given on p.10, and grid references are given for place names as they occur.

Nature of records The majority of records included are casual records, submitted as and when the animal or its sign was seen. Some result from Highland contributions to more targeted national surveys of individual species (e.g. bats, badgers, fox, water shrews). Others come from the published literature (e.g. McGhie, 2002). We have not attempted to collate ALL records from surveys carried out by other organisations. This had been our original intention, but with technological advances in data management since 1999, primarily the inception of the National Biodiversity Network Gateway, the risk of proliferating duplicate records within national databases was considered too great. The HBRG records used in this atlas have been uploaded onto the NBN Gateway and can be viewed there in conjunction with other datasets. Our intention is to continue uploading HBRG mammal records to the NBN Gateway in future, and to provide a link to the updated dataset via the HBRG website.

Number of records The maps in this Atlas are based on a total of more than 25,000 records, submitted by more than 1,200 people. Coverage between species is uneven, with far more records submitted for the rarer and/or more conspicuous species, such as otter and pine marten, than for commoner but less spectacular species such as mice, voles and shrews. See Fig. 1 on p.7.

Geographical coverage We have managed to get SOME mammal records for most of the 351 10km squares in Highland. But this does not amount to comprehensive coverage of the mammal fauna. Also, this kind of recording measures only the range of a species, not its population density. For species occurring at very low densities, such as otter, one individual may account for records in more than one 10km square. See map on p. 8.

Highland mammals and their habitats Unlike the more densely populated (with humans) and intensively developed areas further south, Highland has managed to retain populations of some mammals which have disappeared from most of the rest of Britain (e.g. red squirrel, pine marten and wildcat). The wide variety of habitat types offers the opportunity to encounter different assemblages of mammals and, for some species, the best chance in Britain of being able to view them. Encountering a red squirrel or pine marten in a native pinewood, watching an otter fishing in a west coast sea-loch, or hearing red deer stags roaring on the hill during the rut are special Highland experiences. Wildlife tourism is becoming an increasingly important contributor to the Highland economy, alongside the more traditional mammal-based economic activities such as deer stalking.

How you can contribute As you will see, this Atlas is far from being the last word on Highland mammals! Also, the Mammal Society is about to embark on recording for a new national (GB) Mammal Atlas, to which HBRG will contribute. So please continue to send in records. As always, these should consist of four components:

        Who - the identity of the observer (and a verifier if possible)
        What – the species which you identified
        When – a date, as specific as possible
        Where – a location, preferably with a place name and National Grid
        Reference from an Ordnance Survey map.

Any additional notes or comments, such as the number of animals seen, or habitat details, are always welcome and give the record more context. Records may be submitted via the HBRG website www.hbrg.org.uk or sent to records@hbrg.org.uk .

Highland mammal history

A variety of sources can be used to gain an insight to the history of the Highland mammal fauna. Archaeological work at sites such as the bone caves (NC2626) at Inchnadamph (Lawson, 1995) or High Pasture Cave in Skye (Steven Birch, pers. comm.) has recorded the existence of long extinct species such as polar and brown bears, reindeer, arctic fox and collared lemming, along with others that survived until more recently, such as lynx and wolf. Gaelic place names give some clues to the occurrence of mammals considered noteworthy before written records began, although care is needed in their interpretation. Examples include *Eas an Taghainn* (waterfall of the marten) at NC2206 and *Eilean nan Ròn* (seal island) at NC6465 (and elsewhere).

Some early writers left accounts of mammals, but it is sometimes difficult to know exactly which species they meant. Hector Boece, Bishop of Aberdeen, described the fauna of the Loch Ness area in 1527 as including "martrikis, bevers, quhitredis, and toddis". A century later, Sir Robert Gordon, in his "Earldom of Sutherland" in 1630 lists "Reid Deir and Roes, Woulffs, Foxes, Wyld Catts, Brocks, Skuyrells, Whitretts, Weasels, Otters, Martrixes, Hares and Foumarts". Whilst some names are recognisable to us, others are less so.

The first systematic attempt to gather together information about the mammals of Scotland was the magnificent series of regional vertebrate faunas written by JA Harvie-Brown and his collaborators in the late 19th and early 20th centuries. Five of these cover parts of Highland (Buckley & Harvie-Brown, 1884; Harvie-Brown, 1892; Harvie-Brown, 1895; Harvie-Brown & Buckley, 1897; Harvie-Brown & MacPherson, 1904) and are valuable sources of information on the status of the species at that time. Information on species of particular significance to man, is summarised in Ritchie (1920). Old newspaper articles, such as those assembled by Clark & Sellers (2005), contain fascinating snippets of information. A modern scientific overview of British mammalian history is given by Yalden (1999).

Early scientific research in Highland focused on the evolution of regional and island races of small mammals. Barrett-Hamilton and Hinton (1911-1921) give details of such races. Berry (1996) has a modern summary of views on Scottish island races and their origins. Attention then turned towards the ecology and distribution of small mammals (e.g. Delany & Bishop, 1960; Delany, 1961). More recently, the University of Aberdeen has been particularly active, with a Field Station in Cromarty working on seals (and cetaceans), and other workers concentrating on water voles and American mink. On Rum, long-term studies on red deer are carried out by Cambridge and Edinburgh Universities. Recent advances in molecular genetics have enabled more insight to be gained into the post-glacial history of some mammal species (e.g. Searle et al., 2009). New technologies such as bat detectors and camera traps offer new possibilities for investigating our mammal fauna. No doubt there is a lot more to be revealed as these techniques develop.

Acknowledgements

This has been an entirely voluntary project, so thanks are due to every one of the large number of people who have contributed their time, expertise and enthusiasm in so many different ways. The editor would like to thank: all of the species account authors for their contributions (see contents list); the photographers for the use of their photos and especially James A Moore for the cover photo; Murdo Macdonald for operating the database and producing the maps; Alan Morton the author of DMAP www.dmap.co.uk, which was used to make them; Ruairidh MacIlleathain for advising on the Gaelic species names; Steven Birch for archaeological information; Sue Marrs for assistance with the final production; and David McAllister for compiling the index and proof-reading the whole text. Any remaining errors are the editor's responsibility.

Without funding we would not have been able to print the Atlas, so thanks are due to our co-funders: Inverness Field Club; Tain & District Field Club; BRISC (Biological Recording in Scotland) and four anonymous individual donors.

Without records, there would be no Atlas, so a big THANK-YOU to the 1,200+ mammal enthusiasts who contributed records – whether one, a hundred or a thousand, all are valued. For reasons of space it is only possible to name those who contributed more than 50 records; Ian Anderson, Jane Arnold, Brian Ballinger, the late Barbara Ballinger, Allan Bantick, Charlie Bateman, Saranne Bish, JP Blunt, Will Boyd-Wallis, Stephen Bungard, Pat Cottis, Roger Cottis, John Chester, Derek Crawley, Sally Cuthbertson, Becks Denny, MSC Elliott, Ian Evans, Pat Evans, Mike Fitch, Susan Gallagher, Claire Geddes, David Glass, A Glynne-Percy, Justin Grant, J&R Green, C Griffin, Linda Henderson, David Hetherington, Martin Hind, Rosemary Holt, Alan Horner, Eleanor Hunton, David Jardine, Dave Jones, Peter Kohn, Mary Legg, Howard Loates, J&B Lunn, Liz MacDonald, Murdo Macdonald, David McAllister, Henry McGhie, Jimmy McKellar, Bob McMillan, Trisha Mellish, Jon Mercer, Derek Miller, Donald Mitchell, Stephen Moran, Brian Neath, Pat Newman, the late Gill Nisbet, David O'Brien, Jane O'Donovan, Don O'Driscoll, David Patterson, Neil Redgate, Gwen Richards, Michael Richardson, Bill Richmond, MM Rigby, Liz Rollinson, Ro Scott, Nigel Smith, RJ Stewart, Rob Strachan, Andy Summers, Marina Swanson, Sue Tarr, Jim Teesdale, John Turner, Jeff Waddell, Lyn Wells, Laura Winter, Anne Youngman, Ron Youngman and Grace Yoxon. Thanks also to Scottish Natural Heritage, Highland Bat Groups and the Bat Conservation Trust (National Bat Monitoring Programme) for extra bat records.

The editor thanks all concerned for their patience in waiting for this project to come to fruition! If anyone has been inadvertently left out, I apologise and thank you for your contribution, whatever it was. Finally, I thank Charlie for his support and forbearance during my prolonged sojourns in the study.

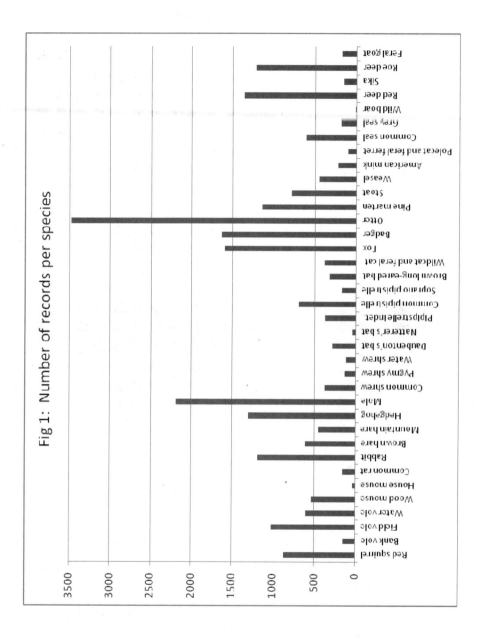

Fig 1: Number of records per species

Map of Atlas coverage

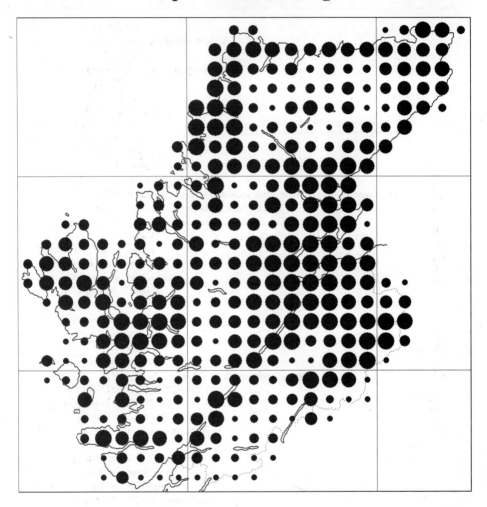

Number of mammal species recorded in each 10km square of the National Grid

Number of species from smallest to largest dots: 1-3; 4-6; 7-9; 10-12; 13-15; 16-18; 19-21; 22-24; 25-31.

Prefix letters for the nine 100km squares shown in the above map are:

NB	NC	ND
NG	NH	NJ
NM	NN	NO

Explanation of the Species Accounts and Maps

The order of the species accounts, and the scientific nomenclature, follows that of the 4th Edition Handbook of British Mammals (Harris & Yalden, 2008). This begins with the rodents, and will be unfamiliar to most mammalogists, who are used to finding the insectivores at the start of such accounts. Alternative Latin name(s) are only given if in recent usage.

Conservation status Gives details of any legislation to which the species is subject; plus details of any conservation policy priority listings. The following gives a brief summary of what these mean, but is not a definitive guide to the law. For more detail consult http://www.snh.gov.uk/protecting-scotlands-nature/protected-species/

Legislation:
Bern Convention Appendix III: species whose status and exploitation may be subject to consideration (now largely implemented via the EHD)
EHD = European Habitats and Species Directive:
> Annex II: species for which Special Areas of Conservation must be designated
> Annex IV: European Protected Species (EPS)
> Annex V: species whose exploitation may be subject to management measures
W&C Act = Wildlife & Countryside Act 1981 (as amended)
> Schedule 5: species which are fully protected (those which are now EPS have been removed from this Schedule)
> Schedule 6: animals protected from prohibited methods of capture
> Schedule 9: non-natives which it is prohibited to release into the wild
WANE Act = Wildlife and Natural Environment (Scotland) Act 2011: supersedes parts of the W&C Act.
MSA = Marine Scotland Act 2010: protects seals from killing, injuring or taking, except under licence or to prevent suffering.

Conservation policy priority lists:
IUCN Red Data List: an international conservation priority listing – all mammals in this Atlas are classified as 'least concern' apart from the otter.
UKBAP = UK Biodiversity Action Plan Priority Species
SBL = Scottish Biodiversity List: species of principal importance for biodiversity conservation in Scotland under the Nature Conservation (Scotland) Act 2004. Includes a 'social criterion' - the top ten species voted for by the Scottish public.
SNH SAF = Scottish Natural Heritage Species Action Framework: species prioritised for practical management action during 2007-12.

Recognition and signs Details of the appearance of the animal and its signs, and an indication of which are reliable identification points for differentiating between similar species. Use alongside a good field guide is recommended!

Ecology and behaviour A summary of the species' habitat, diet, breeding cycle and behaviour which help to explain what you may see throughout the year.

History in Highland A summary of what is known of the species' history in Highland, based on the sources given on p.5.

Past and current management Whether and how management by humans has affected the species in the past and continues to do so in the present.

Current distribution A description of the species' distribution within Highland, including its occurrence on islands.

Nature of records An analysis (based on all records in the HBRG database for which the nature of the record was given) of the major types of record contributing to the distribution map (e.g. live sighting, road casualty, signs etc.).

Distributional trends A description of how the distribution in this Atlas compares with that in the previous ITE Mammal Atlas of 1993 (Arnold, 1993).

Where to look A note to assist you in finding this species in Highland.

Fascinating fact An interesting snippet of information about the species.

Maps All maps show records at 10km square resolution, and in two age-classes: Grey dot = 1999 and before; Black dot = 2000 and after.

Locations of the smaller islands mentioned in the text

Canna	NG20	Rona (south)	NG65
Carna (L Sunart)	NM65	Rum	NM39
Crowlins	NG63	Scalpay (Skye)	NG63
Eigg	NM48	Soay (Skye)	NG41
Gruinard	NG99	Soyea (Lochinver)	NC02
Handa	NC14	St. Kilda (not Highland)	NF09
Muck	NM47	Stroma	ND37
Pabay (Skye)	NG62	Tanera Beag (Summer Isles)	NB90
Raasay	NG53,NG54	Tanera Mor (Summer Isles)	NB90
Ristol	NB91		

Red squirrel
Sciurus vulgaris Linnaeus, 1758

Order: Rodentia
Gaelic: feòrag ruadh

Conservation status W&C Act Schedule 5; UK BAP; SBL; SNH SAF

Recognition and signs Red squirrels can vary greatly in colour, from bright ginger to greyish-brown, being brightest just after their spring moult and darkest in autumn/winter. Their distinctive bushy tails may become bleached to almost white over the summer, when the ear tufts also disappear, to be replaced in the autumn moult. There is scope for confusion between greyer-coloured red squirrels and grey squirrels. Grey squirrels are, on average, larger than reds and never have ear-tufts. One's attention may be drawn to the presence of a squirrel by its 'chacking' warning signal.
When feeding on conifer cones squirrel feeding signs are distinctive. Cones are stripped of their scales leaving a ragged appearance, different from the smooth cone-cores left by mice. (See Plate I.)
Hazel nuts are bitten neatly in half (but beware – great tits also do this).

Ecology and behaviour The red squirrel is found in both coniferous and deciduous woods and plantations. It feeds mainly on seeds and fruits with fungi in season. It therefore requires a mix of tree species to supply food all year round. It is less efficient than the grey squirrel at utilising acorns, which is why the grey squirrel is able to out-compete it in deciduous woodlands. The squirrel habit of caching stores of nuts and seeds for later use probably benefits woodland regeneration.
Red squirrels' dreys (nests) are usually made high in the tree-tops but close to the trunk (unlike birds' nests which are positioned nearer the extremities). The squirrel year begins in spring when mating chases may be seen. Females can have two litters per year, of up to 6 kits each, but a single litter is probably the norm. Most young are born in March/April, begin leaving the nest at about 7 weeks old and are fully weaned at 8-10 weeks. Approximately 80% of young do not survive their first winter. Home-range sizes vary according to habitat quality but can be from 9 to 30ha in coniferous forests (Halliwell, 1997). Red squirrels become less active in winter, but do not actually hibernate.

History in Highland Having colonised Britain after the end of the last ice age, the fortunes of the red squirrel have mirrored those of its woodland habitat. As woodlands have become more fragmented, red

11

squirrels have declined. They were thought to have become extinct in the Highlands during the 18th century and several reintroductions were made. There is now a suspicion that some native red squirrels may have survived. The advent of commercial conifer forestry, firstly by private estates and, after 1919, by the Forestry Commission, marked a change in the red squirrels' fortunes by creating large areas of potential habitat, particularly in the eastern Highlands.

Past and current management Bark stripping by red squirrels was considered so damaging to estate forestry plantations at the turn of the 20th century that a Highland Squirrel Club was established by landowners to pay a bounty for killing them. Details of the tens of thousands which were culled are given in Collier and McGhie (2003). Now conservation management is the priority. The main threat is colonisation of Highland by the non-native grey squirrel which, as well as out-competing the red in certain habitats, also carries the squirrel pox virus which is lethal to red squirrels. Highland is the grey-free stronghold of the red squirrel in Scotland, and securing its future is our responsibility. Habitat fragmentation is still a serious threat, and further built development in prime squirrel habitat could be detrimental. Rope bridges for squirrels have been erected across some roads, such as the B852 at Dores, where road casualties were frequent. Currently (2006 to 2012) the 'Red Squirrels of the Highlands' project employs a project officer, based with the Forestry Commission in Dingwall, whose job is to: encourage the reporting of both red and grey squirrel sightings; encourage monitoring of red squirrel populations by volunteers using a rigorous protocol (Gurnell et al., 2001); promote red squirrel conservation to landowners and encourage appropriate habitat management; and to attempt to limit the incursion of grey squirrels into Highland by maintaining a *cordon sanitaire* along the likely routes of colonisation (river valleys from the south and east). Seven of the identified Scottish red squirrel stronghold areas, where management to favour red squirrels will be a priority, are in Highland (SNH & FCS, 2011).

Current distribution Red squirrels are relatively common in Strathspey and the Black Isle, but rarer elsewhere in Highland. The record for NH18 around Dundonnell in Wester Ross, represents a population resulting from the successful translocation of east-coast squirrels (trapped under licence) in 2008/9 by the Highland Foundation for Wildlife, working with Dundonnell Estate.

12

Nature of records Most red squirrel records (66%) are of live sightings, often crossing roads or in gardens at nut feeders (see Plate I); 20% are road casualties; and 14% are made from signs such as feeding remains or dreys.

Distributional trends The apparent increase in distribution (88 10km squares compared to 45) since the ITE Atlas, may reflect more concerted recording effort, but probably also the success of conservation measures.

Where to look The 'Red Squirrels of the Highlands' project is currently setting up a suite of red squirrel 'hot spots' around the Highlands, where people will be able to view red squirrels in the wild. A new leaflet showing locations will be produced by the end of 2011. Keep an eye on the website for updates. Otherwise, native pinewoods, or forestry plantations with a variety of conifer species, and broadleaved woods such as those along the south side of Loch Ness, are the best places to look for red squirrels. Squirrels are particularly obvious in spring when they are actively pursuing mates.

Fascinating fact HBRG's red squirrel records include several instances of squirrels seen carrying food items in their mouths – hazel nuts, fungi, pine cones, beech mast and in one case a young bird or mouse.

Grey squirrel
Sciurus carolinensis Gmelin, 1788

Order: Rodentia
Gaelic: feòrag ghlas

Conservation status W&C Act Schedule 9; WANE Act

The grey squirrel is a native of North America and was introduced to Britain in the late 19th Century. So far as we know, it has not yet established a population in Highland, but is getting perilously close. Two authenticated grey squirrels have been reported in Highland, one in Strathnairn (NH63) in 2008 and one in Skye in (NG62) 2010. Both probably arrived with human assistance. Both were trapped and killed. Any sightings of grey squirrels should be reported immediately to the Red Squirrel Project Officer (website on p. 139).

Red squirrel

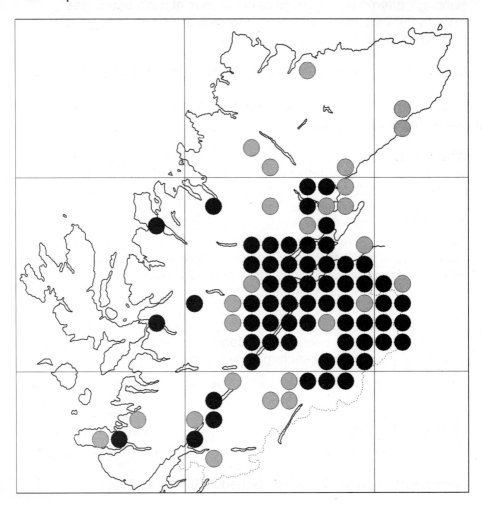

Grey dot = 1999 and before
Black dot = 2000 and after

Bank vole

Order: Rodentia

Myodes glareolus (Schreber, 1780)   Gaelic: famhalan-bruaich
Previous name: *Clethrionomys glareolus* (Tilesias, 1850)

Conservation status None

Recognition and signs A typical vole, with small eyes and ears and blunt nose. Distinguished from field vole by a chestnut/reddish colouring on the back and by its longer tail. The tail is about half of the head and body length, compared to one-third in the field vole. Weight 20-30g. Can be reliably identified from live trapping and from remains in owl pellets or predator scats. Droppings are slightly smaller and usually darker than those of field vole, but this comparison is difficult unless both are present. Distinctive feeding signs are left on hazel nut shells. The bank vole leaves a hole with a chiselled inner edge (like the milling on a coin) but without gnaw-marks on the outer surface (in contrast to the wood mouse).

Ecology and behaviour Lives wherever there is dense cover; in woodlands, scrub, field margins, under gorse or long heather, but less frequently in grassland. Feeds on seeds, berries, leaves and stems, fungi and some invertebrates, taking more green plant material than the wood mouse. Home range size varies with habitat type but can be between 250 and 2000m^2, with males having larger home ranges than females. Bank voles are prolific breeders and a female may produce litters of up to 5 young at approximately monthly intervals throughout the spring and summer. The young can breed at 2 months old. Few bank voles survive two winters. Like the other small rodents, they are a valuable food source for many avian, mammalian and reptilian predators including raptors, owls, wildcats, weasels, stoats, pine martens, foxes and adders.

History in Highland As a forest animal, the bank vole would have spread across Britain with its woodland habitat after the last glaciation. There are archaeological records from the Mesolithic. Recent genetic work (Searle *et al.* 2009) suggests that there may have been two waves of colonisation, resulting in a 'Celtic fringe' of genetically distinct voles in the north. Early literature records are unreliable because some authors failed to differentiate between different vole species, or even between voles and mice.

Past and current management Can be a pest during woodland establishment if its gnawing ring-barks young trees, but in Britain the bank vole does not undergo the drastic population cycles, which result in periodic 'vole plagues' of the field vole.

Current distribution Definitely under-recorded, and is probably present in suitable habitat throughout mainland Highland. Recorded only from Raasay among the islands. Raasay voles are considered by some authors to be a sub-species - *Myodes glareolus erica*. Also reported from Handa in the 1993 Atlas; Scalpay and Skye by Berry (1983), but no recent records from these islands. – Occasional live voles could be dropped by raptors, without establishing a population.

Nature of records More than half of records are from domestic cat kills (34%) or live sightings, often at bird feeders (24%). Remains in owl pellets or predator scat (17%), voles trapped alive or dead (11%), feeding remains (8%) or voles found dead (6%) comprise the rest.

Distributional trends Recorded from a similar number of 10km squares (45) in the ITE Atlas and here. Both cases undoubtedly represent serious under-recording.

Where to look One of the more difficult Highland mammals to see! In suitable habitat bank voles can be encouraged by feeding at a 'mammal table'. They can be active at any time of day or night.

Bank vole

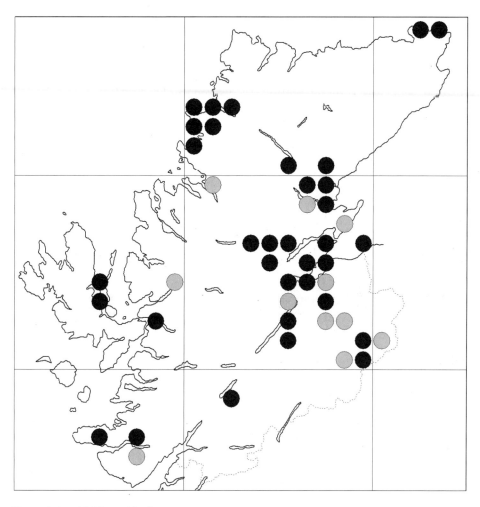

Grey dot = 1999 and before
Black dot = 2000 and after

Field vole

Microtus agrestis (Linnaeus, 1761)   Gaelic: famhalan-feòir
Previous name: short-tailed field mouse (in earlier times people did not distinguish mice from voles)

Conservation status None

Recognition and signs Mouse-sized, but with a blunt snout and short ears; back yellowish- or greyish-brown; tail only 30% length of head and body (contrast with bank vole); weight 25-30g (- 50g in Highland!) The field vole makes characteristic burrows, or 'runs', through dense vegetation, and signs are most easily found by parting grass or rush tussocks to reveal the accumulations of fresh bright-green droppings 6-7mm in length (compared to 8-12mm for water vole) in discrete areas of these runs. Another sign of occupation is the presence of rush or grass stems chopped to lengths of a few cm (also similar to water vole signs).

Ecology and behaviour The field vole prefers reasonably well-drained rough grassland, and avoids boggy places. Burrow systems can also be found in tall heather, particularly where it is mixed with purple moor-grass (*Molinia caerulea*), though the characteristic dung must be used to differentiate field voles from wood mice or bank voles, which inhabit similar places. On the Stoer peninsula (NC03) burrows were found in a dense sward of wavy hair-grass (*Deschampsia flexuosa*) and great wood-rush (*Luzula sylvatica*) in a gulley on steep cliffs normally inaccessible to sheep. On clifftops, near Stoer Lighthouse, and on the north coast, as at Strathy Lighthouse (NC8269), field voles inhabit burrows opening off narrow gulleys in areas of close-cropped hummocky grassland, a habitat I have seen described nowhere else. Field voles can live in suitable habitat from sea level to the high tops. In the corries on the north side of Glas Bheinn (NC22) they inhabit vegetated boulder scree at over 600m; they have been trapped at 720m above Craig Fhiaclach in the Cairngorms (Corbet, 1979); and runs have been found at nearly 900m (3000ft) on Ben Hope (Donald Mitchell, pers. comm.). They may well be more widespread in such places. In hard winters field voles can be active whilst hidden beneath snow cover, and extensive run systems may be revealed when it thaws.
The field vole has a phenomenal reproductive capacity and the pre-breeding population may increase ten-fold by the end of the summer. They are also subject to population fluctuations over several years, and

are visibly more evident in some years than others. Nests are found in rush or grass tussocks, or under discarded or wind-blown sheets of timber or corrugated iron. Litters of up to 8 young may be born at intervals of 6 weeks. Females may become sexually mature at 4 weeks old. Four species of fleas have been collected from field vole nests, all associated with a variety of small mammals. Accumulations of field vole dung also provide a specialised habitat for some tiny fungi.

The weasel is a specialist vole predator, but most medium-sized predatory mammals and birds - fox, wildcat, pine marten, badger, stoat, buzzard, kestrel and owls, will also take field voles.

History in Highland Remains of a vole tentatively identified as *Microtus* cf. *agrestis* were found in the 'Cave Earth' in Badger Cave at Creag nan Uamh, Inchnadamph (NC2616), in association with those of the northern vole (*M. oeconomus*) and lemming (*Dicrostonyx torquatus*), suggesting that the species was present in tundra-like conditions shortly after the last retreat of the ice, and presumably ever since.

Past and current management Although vole populations can cause damage to forestry, particularly in peak population years, protection is achieved by applying tree-guards to young trees, rather than by attempting to manage the vole population.

Current distribution Common on the mainland wherever its preferred habitat of rough grassland exists. Absent from all of the larger Highland islands except Skye, Eigg and Muck, but present on some smaller tidal islands close inshore. Some more distant small islands, such as Soyea, off Lochinver, have been investigated, but no signs were found. Also reported from Scalpay by Berry (1983) but we have no records.

Nature of records The majority of field vole records (68%) result from examining likely areas of habitat for field signs as described above. Skulls or teeth identified from predator scats or owl pellets account for 10%; cat (and dog) kills for 8%; live sightings 7%; and animals trapped alive using Longworth or similar traps, or dead in discarded bottles or cans, 3% each.

Distributional trends The higher number of positive squares now (130) compared to 99 in the 1993 ITE Atlas, probably reflects more intensive recording effort rather than any real range expansion. The distribution still tends to reflect the distribution of recorders. – It is difficult to imagine that any 10km square in mainland Highland does not contain some suitable field vole habitat.

Where to look In years of peak population, field voles can be seen running about on the surface in suitable habitat.

Fascinating fact One large female vole (c. 30g) was the last meal of an adder (itself weighing only 90g) found dead on the road in Glenleraig, Assynt (NC1431).

Field vole   Grey dot = 1999 and before   Black dot = 2000 and after

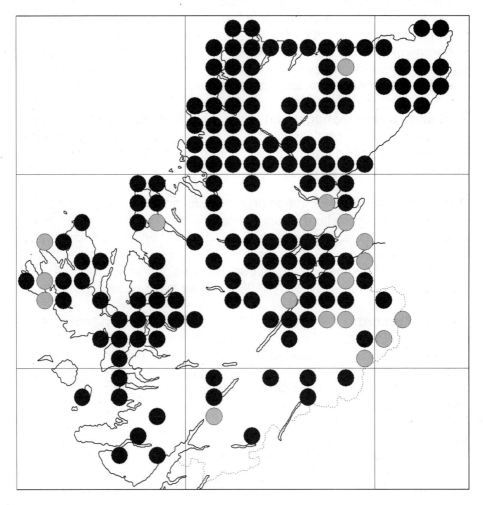

Water vole

Order: Rodentia

Arvicola terrestris (Linnaeus, 1758)   Synonym: *Arvicola amphibius*
Gaelic: famhalan-uisge, radan-uisge, rodan-uisge
Previous name: water rat

Conservation status W&C Act Schedule 5 (full protection since 2008); UK BAP; SBL; SNH SAF

Recognition and signs Britain's largest vole, water voles can reach the size of a rat (140-350g) but are distinguished from rats by their blunt rounded noses, small tucked-in ears and hairy tails about half the length of their bodies. Throughout most of their range they have reddish brown fur but in Highland many individuals are black. Although competent swimmers they are not especially adapted to an aquatic life and do not have webbed feet.

The presence of water voles is indicated by their burrows (4-8cm wide, in contrast to 2-3cm for bank or field vole burrows), which typically drop vertically down into the ground within a few metres of the water's edge. At occupied sites runs (5-9cm wide) are often obvious in the vegetation, joining burrow entrances and points of access to the water. Droppings are similar in shape to those of field vole, cylindrical with blunt ends, but much bigger, being approximately 5mm wide and 10mm long. Brownish green in colour, they are often deposited in latrines which are flattened piles of droppings at the entrance to burrows, along runs, or on ledges and stones at the water's edge. Small cropped areas of vegetation around burrow entrances, known as 'lawns', are most often found at nesting burrows, where the female has been feeding but staying close to the burrow. Feeding remains, neat piles of sections of vegetation typically 10cm long, are similar to those of field or bank vole (Ryland & Kemp 2009) and are not, on their own, reliable indicators of water vole presence. (See Plate I for pictures of signs.)

Ecology and behaviour Water voles prefer deep (>1m) slow flowing water preferably <3m wide with broad swathes of lush, grassy bank side vegetation for foraging and cover, accessible steep banks of earth or peat soft enough for burrowing and allowing refuge during flooding and relatively deep water (>1m). They avoid steep, rocky, over grazed, trampled, fast flowing or over shaded sites. Although often thought of as lowland animals, water voles can be found at up to 1,000m in the smallest headwaters of river systems. In such upland areas, small

21

patches of suitable habitat are separated by large stretches of unsuitable terrain (Lambin et al in press). These patches can only support small populations of water voles, which are very susceptible to extinction from naturally occurring predation, flooding and disease. However, water voles can compensate for this by dispersing over surprisingly long distances. Radio tracking has shown that they travel along waterways and overland, and can create temporary refuges in less suitable habitat. They may travel hundreds of metres in one day (Fisher at al 2009), achieving total distances of up to 23.9km (Lambin *et al.*, 2004; Lambin *et al.*, In press). This allows the many small sub-populations to function overall as a metapopulation.

Female water voles arrange themselves linearly along water ways, holding distinct territories 20-460m long, depending on habitat quality and population density. Males don't defend territories but may share larger home ranges (60-300m) with one or two other males and several females. Both sexes scent mark at latrines. Females may have up to 2-5 litters of 3-8 young each in a year, between May and August. In upland areas litters are fewer and smaller. Gestation lasts 20-22 days and juveniles are independent after 14 days. Most are not sexually mature until after the first winter though young born before July may breed in the same year. Animals born early in the season disperse from about 4 months old while those born later remain near the natal site in summer and autumn. They may survive up to 2 winters, rarely 3. In spring and summer water voles feed on grasses, sedges, rushes and herbaceous species, whereas in winter, when they spend long periods below the surface, they feed on roots, rhizomes, bulbs and food stored below ground.

Water voles experience a naturally high rate of predation by weasel, stoat, otter, brown rat, fox, heron, birds of prey and pike. Less naturally, American mink, and in some areas cats, can have a significant impact. Female mink are small enough to follow a water vole into its burrow.

History in Highland Abundant fossils show water vole presence in Britain during both glacial and interglacial periods. Genetic analysis (Piertney *et al.*, 2005) indicates that Scottish populations recolonised after the last ice age from the Iberian peninsula, and are distinct from English and Welsh water voles that originated from eastern Europe. Knowledge of water vole distribution in the Highlands was sketchy until relatively recently, although Darling and Boyd (1964) had noted their presence in the limestone areas of Durness and Assynt and MacNally

(1968) mentions black water voles as prey at eyries of golden eagle in Culachy forest south east of Loch Ness.

Past and current management Highland water voles have not been as severely affected by development pressures as those further south. However habitats have been impacted by afforestation, muirburn, overgrazing, engineering, dredging, hydro schemes, pollution etc. Legal protection means that detailed surveys must now be undertaken before any development (e.g. wind farms) and mitigation steps taken. This has also led to increase in recording. Habitat management recommendations are given in Strachan and Moorhouse (2006). Key management for water voles is the control of mink where they already occur and preventing them from expanding into areas that are currently mink free. After two initial mink monitoring and control projects, in the Cairngorms and North-west Highland, a new project began in 2011 aiming at strategic mink control across the whole of northern Highland (see American mink species account for details, p.105).

Current distribution Water voles are far more widespread in mainland Highland than was previously thought, with scattered records in both upland and lowland areas (Woodroffe 2000). Not recorded from any of the Highland islands. Higher densities are found in Caithness and West Sutherland where more systematic surveys and research have been undertaken. Water voles are likely to be under recorded in many areas and, where suitable habitat exists, gaps are probably more likely to indicate lack of records rather than absence. In river systems where mink are present, water voles tend to be absent from the main stem and larger tributaries and are restricted to the headwaters and smaller tributaries. They appear to be more frequent in the mink free areas in the north of Highland, than within the current range of mink in the south.

Nature of records Most records (90%) are of field signs (burrows, runs, droppings and feeding remains). Live sightings comprise 5%; cat/dog kills 2%; animals found dead 2%; recorded as prey and 'caught' <1% each.

Distributional trends Water voles are recorded in 132 10 km squares now as opposed to 20 in the 1993 atlas. This is most likely due to increased recording effort, rather than any real range expansion.

Where to look Water voles are active during daylight and spend 25-30% of a 24 hour period outside their burrows during the breeding season. Sit quietly at the bank side close to signs of an active colony especially during early morning or evening and you may see them.

Fascinating fact Water voles have been found on an area of machair in NW Sutherland more than 100m from the nearest waterway. This is a rare occurrence in the UK, but common in continental Europe.

Water vole   Grey dot = 1999 and before   Black dot = 2000 and after

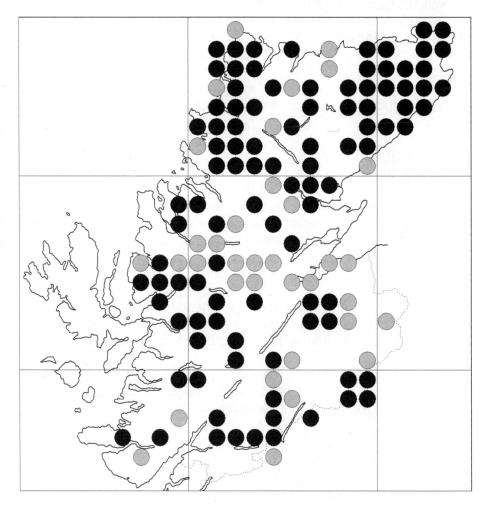

Wood mouse

Order: Rodentia

Apodemus sylvaticus (Linnaeus, 1758)
Synonym: long-tailed field mouse   Gaelic: luch-fheòir, luchag-fheòir

Conservation status None

Recognition and signs A lively mouse with a long tail, large ears and prominent eyes. Body brown above and grey beneath. About 150 - 200mm long, of which the tail is almost half. Adult weight from 13 to 27g. Males are on average slightly larger than females. Mice from island populations tend to be larger than mainland mice.
Can be reliably identified by live-trapping, from food remains (hazel nuts) and from skulls in owl pellets. When feeding on hazel nuts, wood mice leave a hole with a chiselled inner edge (like the milling on a coin) and gnaw-marks around the outside of the hole. These distinguish the work of the wood mouse from that of the bank vole. Wood mice may also strip fallen pine/fir/spruce cones for their seeds, and leave a more closely-cropped core than squirrels (see Plate I). Cannot reliably be identified from droppings, which are similar to those of house mouse. Tracks showing an imprint of the tail between the hind feet may be seen in snow or mud where the mouse has hopped from one hole to another.

Ecology and behaviour Prefers habitats with good cover, such as hedgerows, scrub, woodlands and arable fields in summer. Lives on the ground surface in dense vegetation or thick leaf litter, and also burrows below ground. Nests are composed of leaves and moss. Feeds on seeds fruits, invertebrates, fungi and occasionally carrion. Often caches food (even inside houses). Home range size depends on habitat quality and the age of the individual, with juveniles occupying smaller ranges than sexually mature animals. Male ranges tend to overlap with others of either sex, but females exclude other females during the breeding season. Home range sizes can vary from less than 1ha to 3-4 ha. Breeding takes place throughout the summer and each female will have several litters in a season. Females can breed from the age of 7 weeks. Pregnancy lasts about 3 weeks and an average litter will contain 4-7 young. Young are weaned at about 18 days. The population reaches its highest density in autumn, when breeding ceases. Few adults will survive the winter to breed another year, but survival of late-born young is good. Arable-living mice tend to move into other habitats after harvest, and can become a problem in houses at this time of year. Wood mice are largely nocturnal, but activity is inhibited by bright moonlight. The wood mouse is preyed upon by a variety of birds and mammals, such as owls, cats, foxes and weasels.

History in Highland Probably one of the earliest colonisers of the mainland after the ice age, and widespread in suitable habitats ever since. Genetic studies suggest that wood mice may have been introduced to Eigg from the mainland, possibly in Viking times, and then spread to the rest of the Small Isles from there (Berry, 2009). By the 19th century faunas the wood mouse was considered 'common' and 'generally distributed'.

Past and current management Regarded as less of a pest than the house mouse, but many anti-house mouse measures (e.g. mouse traps, domestic cats, rodenticides) also work against wood mice. May also fall victim to agricultural practices such as seed dressing and the use of pesticide sprays.

Current distribution Widespread but definitely under-recorded. Occurs on more islands than any of the other small rodents, being present on Skye, Isle Ristol, Rum, Eigg, Muck, Canna and Raasay. Also recorded from Rona and the Crowlins by Berry (1983) but we have no records. Is far commoner in Highland than the house mouse, and frequently comes into houses, particularly in the winter.

Nature of records The majority of records are cat kills (29%) or live sightings (24%).

Distributional trends Recorded from 80 10km squares in ITE Atlas and 94 now, reflecting greater recent recording effort.

Where to look Can be encouraged to visit 'mammal tables' by feeding with peanuts, bird seed or fat cakes.

Fascinating fact When the common rat eradication programme was underway on Canna (see p. 33) a sample of the island's wood mice were taken into custody by the Royal Zoological Society of Scotland, in order to save them from potential annihilation. In the event, mice which remained on the island survived, because some of their home ranges were small enough to lie completely between the poisoned bait stations which were placed at 50m intervals.

Wood mouse

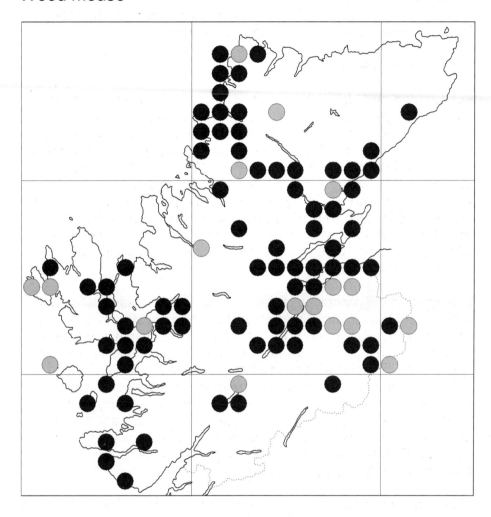

Grey dot = 1999 and before
Black dot = 2000 and after

House mouse

Order: Rodentia

Mus domesticus Rutty 1772   Gaelic: luch-taighe, luchag-taighe
Previous name: *Mus musculus* (Linnaeus 1758)

Conservation status None

Recognition and signs A more staid mouse than the wood mouse
and a duller grey-brown in colour, with less conspicuous eyes and ears.
Slightly smaller than wood mouse (head and body length 70-90mm),
and with a shorter tail. Within Britain, more northerly house mice have
shorter tails in relation to their body length (Berry, 1970). Average
weights 15-20g, with females slightly larger than males.
Identified most readily by trapping (alive or dead), or from skulls in owl
pellets. The incisors have a distinctive notch when viewed from the
side. Droppings are similar to those of the wood mouse. The most
frequently-occurring mouse in Highland houses is the wood mouse – so
beware, not every mouse in a house is a house mouse!

Ecology and behaviour In Highland is found only in association with
humans, but this can be in farm steadings and grain stores as well as
houses. May perhaps 'erupt' from agricultural into domestic premises,
at population peaks. They prefer to feed on cereal grains, but will eat a
wide variety of human foods and animal feed products. Where food is
plentiful house mice can reach high densities, and the concept of
individual home ranges ceases to be valid. They are mainly nocturnal.
House mice can breed at any time of year when living inside buildings.
Each female can have a litter of 5-8 young at approximately monthly
intervals. Gestation lasts 3 weeks, young are weaned at 3 weeks old
and can themselves breed at 5-6 weeks old.

History in Highland The house mouse is native to the Middle East and
is thought to have arrived in Britain via human maritime trade as early
as the Iron Age. Recent genetic analysis (Searle *et al.,* 2009) has
shown that house mice from northern and western locations (including
Caithness, Sutherland and Orkney) are of a different genetic type from
those inhabiting most of the rest of Britain, being more similar to
Norwegian house mice. Their presence is thought to reflect the Viking
influence in these areas. The more recent history of Highland house
mice is largely a mystery. The 19th century faunas describe them as
'common' or 'abundant'. In the absence of humans, house mice are

thought to be out-competed by wood mice, as happened on St. Kilda after the humans left in 1930. Populations of outdoor-living house mice in other parts of Britain are thought to have declined since the invention of the combine harvester led to the demise of farmyard corn-ricks. – The same may be true of Highland.

Past and current management House mice are generally controlled by trapping and/or poisoning wherever found because of their tendency to eat stored food products and contaminate them with urine and faeces, and damage buildings by gnawing through insulation and electric cables.

Current distribution Records are very sporadic on the mainland, and absent from all islands except Skye and Raasay, plus a literature record from Canna (Campbell, 1984). This may reflect its true distribution or the fact that people are reticent to report the presence of house mice!

Nature of records House mice have been recorded from cat kills, live sightings, trapped individuals and literature records, but numbers are too small for meaningful analysis.

Distributional trends Recorded from 25 10km squares in the ITE Atlas and 27 now. Both of these could reflect under-recording, or genuine rarity.

Where to look Around farmyards and steadings, particularly where grain is stored.

Fascinating fact The house mouse is the wild ancestor of all laboratory and fancy (pet) mice.

House mouse

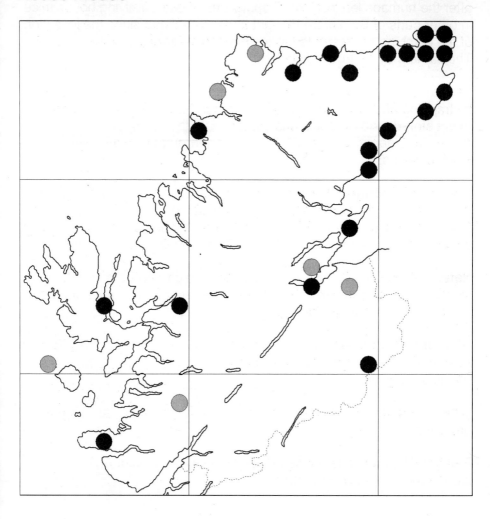

Grey dot = 1999 and before
Black dot = 2000 and after

Common rat

Order: Rodentia

Rattus norvegicus (Berkenhaut, 1769)

Synonym: Norway rat, brown rat

Gaelic: radan, rodan

Conservation status None

Recognition and signs A large mouse-shaped rodent with grey-brown fur above (although colour is not a reliable way to differentiate it from the much rarer Black or Ship rat), a paler grey underside, scaly naked tail, pointed nose and prominent ears. Head and body length up to 250mm (twice that of wood mouse), tail nearly the same again. Can weigh up to 500g, with males on average slightly larger than females. Droppings are larger than those of mice and bank or field voles, but similar in size to those of water vole, about 12 x 4mm. Rat droppings tend to be brown and have pointed ends whereas water vole droppings are greener, with rounded ends. Rats also swim and can be confused with water voles in this situation. The longer tail, more pointed face and more obvious ears and eyes of the rat should be diagnostic.

Ecology and behaviour Common rats are most frequent in areas of human habitation and agricultural activity such as rubbish tips, food stores and farm steadings. Away from buildings they prefer dense cover and may be found living alongside water courses and on the shore. They are omnivorous and will eat almost anything, including grain, fruit, invertebrates and meat. They also cause damage by gnawing electric cables, insulation etc. Rats are creatures of habit and will establish regular run-ways which become well-worn and, inside buildings, marked by greasy deposits. They are largely nocturnal. Given a good food supply, rats can breed all year round, producing litters of up to 9 young after a 22 day gestation period. Young are weaned at 3 weeks and can breed at 3-4 months old.
Rats are eaten by a variety of predators, with the larger ones, such as foxes, taking adults, and smaller predators, such as weasels, concentrating on juveniles. Most rats survive less than one year.

History in Highland The common rat is native to eastern Asia and was only introduced to Britain by shipping (thought to be from Russia, rather than Norway as its alternative name suggests) in the early 18th century, reaching Scotland before 1754. It quickly out-competed the Black or Ship rat (*Rattus rattus*) which had been present in Britain since Roman times. In the faunas, it is described as 'abundant' in most areas, but confined to the coast in the west.

Past and current management Rats are still actively controlled wherever they interfere with human interests. They are very wary of new things appearing in their environment and will taste a small quantity of any new food, and await a reaction, before eating a large amount. In this way they can avoid poisons which require consumption of a large dose for lethality. Modern rat poisons produce delayed symptoms, which mean that the rat finds out too late that it has eaten a fatal dose.

Current distribution Sparsely recorded from mainland Highland and present on Skye, Rum and Eigg. Common rats previously occurred on both Handa and Canna but have recently been eradicated (Stoneman & Zonfrillo, 2005; Bell, 2007) by targeted poisoning, because of the impact they were having on ground-nesting colonial seabirds. Also reported by Berry (1983) from Raasay and Muck, but we have no records.

Nature of records Live sightings comprise the majority of records (43%); with 17% found dead; 15% each trapped or identified from signs; 8% cat kills; and 2% from remains in owl pellets.

Distributional trends Recorded from 59 10km squares in ITE Atlas and 53 now. Both of these probably represent significant under-recording.

Where to look Around grain stores and steadings.

Fascinating fact In the absence of field voles, the rats of the island of Rum extend their distribution out onto the open hill. A research project is underway (2010-12) to determine whether they are having an adverse impact on the colony of manx shearwaters (*Puffinus puffinus*) which nest in burrows high on the hills of Rum.

Common rat

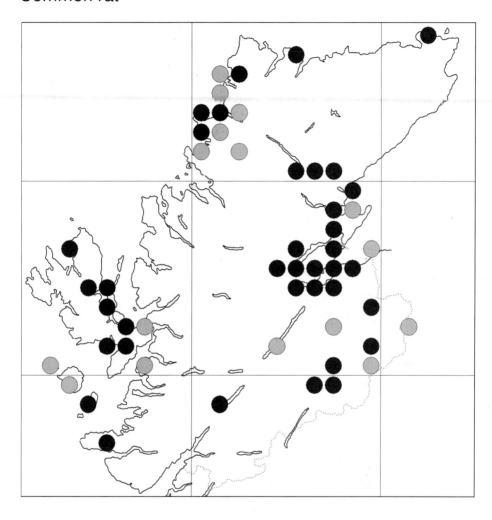

Grey dot = 1999 and before
Black dot = 2000 and after

Rabbit

Order: Lagomorpha

Oryctolagus cuniculus (Linnaeus, 1758)
Synonym: European rabbit, coney   Gaelic : coinean, rabaid

Conservation status None

Recognition and signs Smaller than brown or mountain hares, ears without black tips, and hind legs shorter in relation to body than hares. When running shows white under tail. Mainly greyish brown but considerable variation in colour from light sandy colour to black (melanistic). Underparts white or grey, sometimes with brown chest patch. The nape of the neck has woolly fur which is often reddish. Feet, including soles, are furred and buff coloured. Rabbits moult once a year, beginning at the head in March and spreading rearwards, with the underfur not completely replaced until October-November. Adult head and body length is up to 400 mm. Adult weights 1200-2000g. Rabbit tracks and droppings are distinctive although similar to (but smaller than) those of hares. The track of the hind foot is about 4cm long and 2.5cm broad. Rabbit droppings are about 10mm in diameter and more spherical than hare droppings. Rabbits use droppings for scent marking their territory and, unlike hares, generally deposit them in large quantities, often in scrapes, or on slightly elevated places such as grass tussocks or mole hills. Rabbit burrows are round in section and considerably smaller than badger setts or fox earths.

Ecology and behaviour Rabbits flourish wherever there is short turf for grazing and free-draining soil for burrows. They can live above ground where there is dense cover, such as under gorse bushes. Rabbits will eat grass and crops but they can also do considerable damage by de-barking trees and shrubs in winter. Rabbits have a social hierarchy, with dominant males (bucks) and females (does) occupying the best parts of the warrens and thus breeding more successfully. Females can produce litters of 3-7 young (kits) at 30-day intervals from January to August. As well as marking their territories with droppings, rabbits mark the ground by rubbing it with scent glands under their chin - "chinning". Heavy grazing around a warren leaves short vegetation, enabling rabbits to see predators more easily. Their prominent eyes give a wide angle of view. Most of their day is spent underground, with above-ground activity peaking in the early morning and evening. Rabbits provide an important food source for a wide range of mammals and birds - badgers, wildcats, foxes, stoats, pine martens, eagles, buzzards, red kites and crows. Many of these predators will also take advantage of the numerous roadside casualties.

History in Highland Rabbits are native to the Iberian peninsula, where they are now considered endangered. Thought to have been introduced to England by the Normans, their history in Highland is far more recent. Introductions here began in the early 18th century, with rabbits recorded in Caithness by 1743 but not until 1850 in Wester Ross. The 19th century faunas record them as spreading from east to west along the straths.

Past and present management Having been introduced for their food value, rabbits have proved to be a mixed blessing because of their depredations on pasture and crops. Attempts to control their numbers by shooting, ferreting, snaring and gassing have been largely unsuccessful. Even the introduction of myxomatosis in the 1950s only served as a temporary brake, until resistance to the virus evolved. Severe winters may knock them back temporarily, but because of their enormous reproductive capability, they always bounce back.

Current distribution Widespread on the more fertile and free-draining soils of the more agricultural eastern Highlands and the western crofting areas, but absent from boggy, rocky and mountainous areas. Present on Skye, Raasay, Soay, Eigg, Canna, Gruinard Island, Stroma, and Handa, but absent from Rum. Also reported by Berry (1983) from Rona, the Crowlins, Scalpay and Pabay but we have no records.

Nature of records The majority of records (44%) are from signs; with live sightings 32%; road casualties 22% and predator kills 2%.

Distributional trends Recorded from 195 10km squares in ITE Atlas, and 184 now, probably indicating a fairly stable distribution.

Where to look Rabbits are easy to spot on roadside verges, especially in the early morning and evening.

Fascinating fact The survival of wildcats at Inchnadamph (NC22) in Sutherland in the 1960s was reputed to be because the rabbits there did not catch myxomatosis.

Rabbit

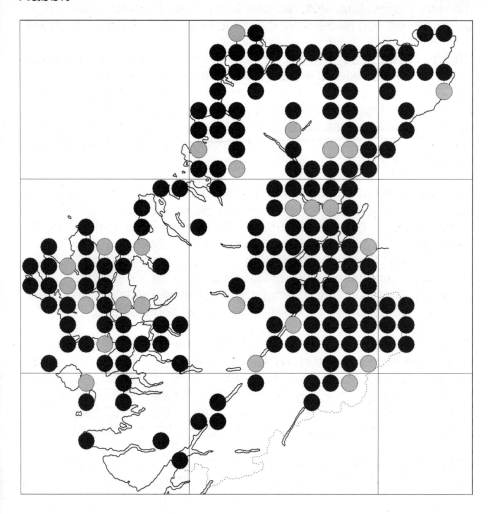

Grey dot = 1999 and before
Black dot = 2000 and after

Brown hare

Order: Lagomorpha

Lepus europaeus (Pallas 1778)
Synonym : common hare, European hare   Gaelic: geàrr, maigheach

Conservation status WANE Act sets close season 1st February – 30th September; UK BAP; SBL

Recognition and signs The brown hare is a much larger animal than the rabbit with longer legs, longer black-tipped ears and an overall red-brown rather than grey-brown colour. It has a leaping stride when running fast and the tail is normally held down with the black and white dorsal surface visible. Many variations in colour are recorded such as melanistic (black), albino and sandy. Moults occur in spring and autumn, with the summer coat being lighter than the redder winter coat. Brown hares weigh 3-4kg, with females averaging slightly more than males. Overall head and body length averages 55cm with a 7cm tail. Tracks leave parallel impressions of the long hind feet (15cm long, 4-5 claw prints visible) placed ahead of staggered oval prints of the forefeet (4cm long, 4 claws). Droppings are larger (at 1 cm) and more flattened than those of rabbit, fibrous and usually brown rather than black. Tracks and droppings are indistinguishable from those of the mountain hare.

Ecology and behaviour The brown hare is largely a lowland animal, living predominantly in arable areas, and feeding on grasses and crop plants. Evidence from the straths south of Inverness suggests that hares spend the winter in woodland and move to arable fields when the crops start growing. In areas where winter-sown cereals are prevalent, such as the Black Isle, they may remain in the fields all year round. Hares become most visible in early spring when mating takes place, but are otherwise largely nocturnal. The widely reported behaviour of two hares "boxing" that gave rise to the expression "mad March hare" was originally thought to be two males (bucks or jacks) fighting, but is now known to be an unreceptive female (doe or jill) resisting the advances of a male. Gestation lasts 37-44 days and the young (leverets) are born, fully-furred, above ground. The female leaves them while she goes to feed and returns only to suckle them. Once weaned, at 5 weeks, they are independent. Each female can have up to 3 litters per year. Brown hares are not always solitary animals, up to twenty have been seen together in snow near Farr (NH63).

History in Highland Brown hares are thought to have been introduced into Britain from mainland Europe in Iron Age or possibly Roman times. They first began to appear in records for the Highlands in the late 18th century. Their spread was reputed to be facilitated by improvements to the road system. (Whether this meant that the hares used the roads, or that better roads facilitated their transport by people, is not made clear.) The 19th century faunas record them 'following cultivation far up the glens' but that in Skye 'the leverets are destroyed by the hordes of curs which the crofters too often keep'.

Past and current management As a game species, brown hares have, over the course of history, been subjected to shooting, snaring and (now illegal) coursing with dogs. Late 20th century changes in agricultural methods have caused a national decline in population density that may be reflected in the more intensively cultivated parts of Highland. Many estates and small shoots no longer shoot brown hares because of this decline.

Current distribution Brown hares are widely distributed throughout the arable areas of Easter Ross and the Black Isle, and up to the north coast in Caithness. The absence of records from the boggier and more mountainous north and west is probably a true reflection of their distribution. Their occurrence on Skye reflects the presence there of more fertile volcanic soils. Brown hares are not present on any of the other Highland islands.

Nature of records The vast majority of records (66%) are of live sightings, with 33% road (and one or two other) casualties, and only 1% from signs.

Distributional trends Recorded from 57 10km squares in ITE Atlas, compared to 88 now. This appears to reflect a fairly stable distribution, with some infilling of gaps due to improved recording effort recently.

Where to look Any mixed grassland and arable areas, particularly in the east of Highland or on Skye, in the summer and especially at dawn and dusk.

Brown hare

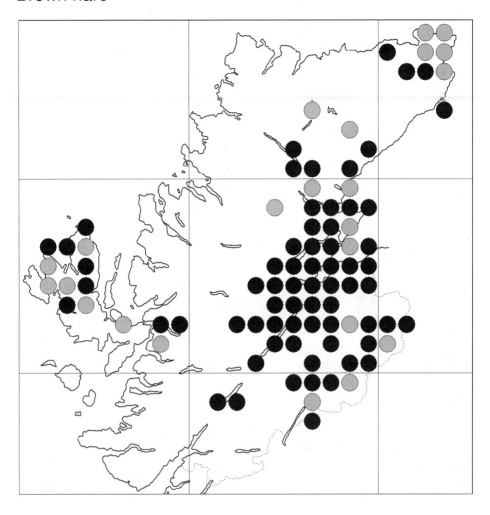

Grey dot = 1999 and before
Black dot = 2000 and after

Mountain hare

Order: Lagomorpha

Lepus timidus Linnaeus 1758 Gaelic: geàrr bhàn, maigheach bhàn
Lepus timidus scoticus (Hilzheimer 1906 Northern Scotland)
Synonym: blue hare, variable hare, Arctic hare, white hare

Conservation status EHD Annex V; WANE Act sets close season 1st March – 31st July; UKBAP; SBL

Recognition and signs The mountain hare is smaller than the brown hare and has relatively shorter ears. The mean weight of males is 2.6 kg and females 2.9 kg. Mean length of body and head is about 50cm plus tail of 6cm. The summer coat is grey-brown, without black grizzling, and the tail all white. Going into the autumn moult, the dusky brown pelage with grey-blue under fur showing through gives rise to the name "blue hare". The winter coat may vary from pure white to a patchy brown and white, especially on the head and neck. This is replaced in the spring moult by the summer coat. Young (leverets) during their first autumn are dark grey/brown, which led to the erroneous belief that mountain hares had a third moult.
The tracks are very similar to those of the brown hare, with the parallel hind feet landing in front of the staggered forefeet. The droppings are indistinguishable from those of the brown hare, being 0.5-1.3 cm in diameter, fibrous in texture and brown to grey green in colour. They are mostly deposited at random while feeding but may be clumped together at resting points such as beside a boulder.

Ecology and behaviour Mountain hares generally occupy drier moorlands over about 300 metres in altitude. They have a diurnal activity pattern, moving downhill at night to feed and uphill at first light, often following well worn tracks. Their main food is grasses, rushes and heather but they will also take bark from a variety of shrubs and trees. Their shelters (forms) are merely depressions in the heather but, combined with the hares' cryptic colouration, these offer excellent concealment from predators such as golden eagles. In at least one area, on the sides of the River Findhorn east of Ruthven (NH83), mountain hares use burrows, and will sit by these during the day and dart into them at any sign of disturbance or danger. It is not clear whether they excavate such burrows or take them over from rabbits. Mountain hares have a high reproductive rate with each female being able to have up to 4 litters of 1-4 leverets between March and August.

History in Highland Unlike the brown hare, the mountain hare is native and, as a tundra animal, was probably one of the earliest colonists of Britain at the end of the last ice age. As a game species it has been moved around by people for sporting purposes, including reportedly being introduced to Skye by a Major Frazer (Harvie-Brown & Macpherson, 1904) and an unsuccessful introduction to the island of Ligg between 1800 and 1900, which accounts for the old record there.

Past and current management Management for sport continues today, particularly in eastern Highland. In the past, mountain hare drives on estates could result in bags of over 200 in a day. Ironically, whilst grouse moor management produces good hare habitat, they are rigorously controlled on some grouse moors because of a link between mountain hares and high tick populations which carry louping-ill, a disease affecting red grouse (Laurenson *et al.*, 2003).

Current distribution The mountain hare's distribution is more-or-less the inverse of that of the brown hare, being found mainly in the more rugged upland parts of Highland. Its preference for drier moorlands is reflected in its absence from the Flow Country of Caithness and Sutherland. Of the islands, it is found only on Skye and Raasay. Also reported from Scalpay by Berry (1983) but we have no records.

Nature of records Identification from signs comprises 46% of records; with 34% live sightings; 19% road casualties and 2% found dead on the hill or shot.

Distributional trends Recorded from 85 10km squares in the ITE Atlas compared to 188 now, probably reflecting increased recording effort. Kinrade et al. (2008) give a report on distribution ascertained from landowner questionnaires.

Where to look Mountain hares may be seen from the roadside, where roads traverse moorland above 300 metres, such as south east of Inverness or the A9 at Drumochter.

Fascinating fact For a period in the early 1920s a population of black mountain hares occurred on the Langwell estate near Dunbeath in Caithness (ND12). These presumably melanistic hares were reported to retain their black coats even in winter (which must have made them very vulnerable to predation).

41

Mountain hare

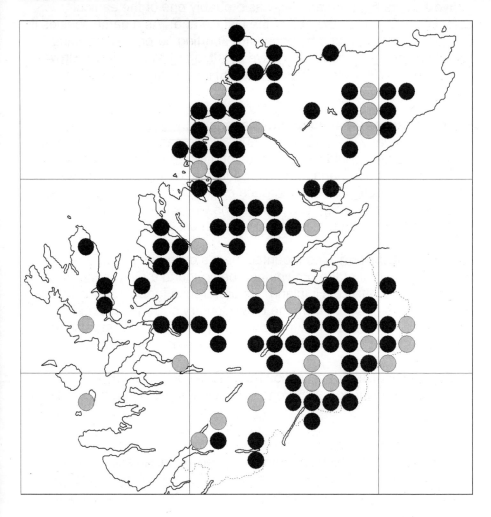

Grey dot = 1999 and before
Black dot = 2000 and after

Hedgehog

Order: Erinaceomorpha
Erinaceus europaeus Linnaeus, 1758
Gaelic: gràineag
Synonym: Western European hedgehog

Conservation status W&C Act Schedule 6; UKBAP; SBL

Recognition and signs Unmistakable - the only British mammal with spines replacing hair on its dorsal surface. It is able to erect its spines when under threat, and roll itself into a ball by tightening the orbicularis muscle which encircles the body at the edge of the spiny area. Adult hedgehogs measure 200-300mm in length (including the tail). Males are, on average, larger than females and can be differentiated by the greater distance between the male's anal and genital openings (if you can get the hedgehog to unroll!) The weight of hedgehogs varies markedly with the seasons, as they emerge from hibernation thin and fatten up over the summer. Droppings measure 15-50mm long by 10mm in diameter and are distinctive when they contain visible invertebrate remains such as fragments of beetle elytra (wing-cases). Tracks are 5-toed and can be confused with those of rats, squirrels and water vole. Hedgehogs can sometimes be detected by the snuffling and snorting noises they make whilst foraging and particularly during courtship.

Ecology and behaviour An insectivore feeding largely on invertebrates, particularly earthworms, beetles, caterpillars, slugs etc. but it will also eat the eggs and chicks of ground-nesting birds. Mainly nocturnal, but juveniles may be active in daylight in autumn as they try to gain weight prior to hibernation. Summer nests, used for daytime rest and breeding, are loosely assembled from leaves and other vegetation. Winter nests for hibernation are similar, but located more securely. Animals emerge from hibernation in April/ May and mating takes place soon afterwards. Litters of 4-6 young are born in mid-summer after a gestation period of 4-5 weeks. The young are suckled for 4-6 weeks and disperse after weaning to seek their own home range. Juveniles must gain a weight of at least 450g if they are to survive hibernation. The sexes lead largely separate lives, but their home ranges may overlap. Nothing is known of population densities or home range sizes in Highland, as no research has been carried out here.

History in Highland Being of no economic importance, records of hedgehogs in the historical literature are few and far between. The first records in the faunas are from the late 19th century. Pennant in "Caledonian Zoology" (1777) says "Not found beyond the Tay, perhaps not beyond the Forth." Hugh Miller, in "My schools and Schoolmasters" (1854) remarks that hedgehogs were unknown in the Cromarty area at that time. Modern commentary (2005) by Clark & Sellers says "Hedgehogs...did not arrive in Caithness until the first half of the 20th century (though whether naturally or with assistance from man is unclear) and now have a thriving population." These statements suggest that the hedgehog could be a relatively recent colonist in the north of Scotland, having spread from the central belt only during the past two hundred years or so. This requires further investigation.

Past and current management Management is more by inadvertence than intent. Hedgehogs are prone to becoming road casualties, and their habit of hibernating in compost heaps and piles of garden refuse leads to unfortunate accidents. Generally regarded as a benign inhabitant of our gardens and waysides, but experience in the Western Isles, where predation by introduced hedgehogs has severely impacted ground-nesting bird populations (Jackson & Green, 2000), shows that any temptation to distribute it to new islands should be strongly resisted.

Current distribution Widely recorded from the more cultivated and populous periphery of the Highland mainland. This probably reflects its true distribution as an inhabitant of woodlands, gardens, roadside verges and hedgerows, which harbour higher densities of its invertebrate prey than more open upland, bog, or intensively arable areas. Widespread in Skye. Introduced to Canna in 1939 (Campbell, 1984). Also recorded from Soay by Berry (1983) and in ITE Atlas (1993), but we have no records. Not recorded from Handa, Stroma, Rum, Eigg or Muck. Possibly recently introduced to Raasay.

Distributional trends Recorded from 108 Highland 10km squares in 1993 Atlas and 167 now. The higher number of positive squares now may reflect increased recording effort, or continuing range expansion.

Nature of records The vast majority of records (84%) are of road casualties, with 15% live sightings and less than 1% each for other casualties and signs (droppings or nests). The distribution of records throughout the year, rising in spring, peaking in summer and tailing off in autumn is typical of a hibernating mammal.

Where to look Hedgehogs can be encouraged to visit your garden by offering food and water. Welfare organisations recommend meaty (rather than fish-based) cat-food and not bread and milk which will cause diarrhoea.

Hedgehog

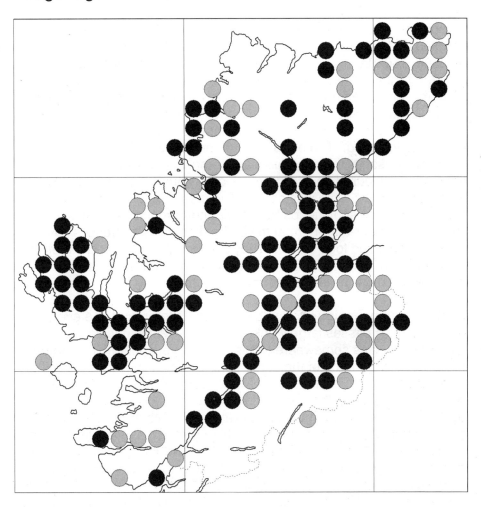

Grey dot = 1999 and before
Black dot = 2000 and after

Mole

Order: Soricomorpha

Talpa europaea Linnaeus, 1758 Previous name: *Talpa europaeus*

Synonym: European mole Gaelic: famh

Conservation status None

Recognition and signs The mole is unlikely to be confused with any other British mammal. With its sausage-shaped body covered in velvety black fur which completely conceals the small eyes and ears, wide flattened forelimbs enabling it to dig the tunnels which it inhabits, and pink flexible snout to seek out its invertebrate prey, the mole is well-adapted for life underground. Adult moles weigh about 100g, and measure 140-180mm long (including the tail) with males being on average slightly larger than females. Because of their unusual sexual anatomy, the sexes are indistinguishable for most of the year. Males have internal testes; females have masculinised external genitalia and internal ovotestes, which secrete male hormones in autumn and female hormones in spring. The perforation of the female's vulva in the breeding season is the only reliable external differentiating feature. Pale cream-coloured (leucistic) moles occasionally occur (two out of 72 records where the mole was seen). The most reliable sign of mole presence are the spoil-heaps from their underground excavations - mole hills. Larger-than-normal mole hills, known as 'fortresses', usually contain a nest and food cache. They are thought to be used as refuges in areas of frequent flooding. Mole skulls and limb-bones can be identified from owl pellets and predator scats.

Ecology and behaviour Being conducted underground, the everyday life of the mole passes largely unknown to us. Moles maintain their tunnels not just as somewhere to live, hidden from potential predators, but as the main source of their food supply - the earthworms and other invertebrates which fall in. If supply exceeds demand, earthworms are immobilised by biting the head, and cached for later consumption. In cold weather, when earthworms retreat deeper into the soil, so do the moles. Hence the proliferation of freshly-erupted molehills during cold spells. Individual moles maintain exclusivity of their tunnels by scent-marking as they patrol their territory. Meetings usually result in aggression. Each mole occupies an area between 0.1 and 1.6 ha, with one or two nest chambers within its tunnel system. Radio-tracking studies have shown that moles have two or three activity periods per day (depending on the season), returning to their nest to rest in between. Males and females lead separate existences except during the breeding season. In spring, a sudden increase in mole-runs is seen, as males travel in search of mates. After mating, the female alone is responsible for tending the young in her underground nest. Here, after a gestation period of 4 weeks, 3-4 young are born and reared until 5-6 weeks old, at which point they disperse to find their own territories. This is the most precarious time for young moles, when mortality rates from predation or starvation can be high.

History in Highland The mole has been present in Britain since the end of the last glaciation, and probably colonised the Highlands as soon as suitable habitat became available. Numbers during the Mesolithic period (when humans were hunter-gatherers) were estimated to be slightly lower than nowadays (Harris & Yalden, 2008), and moles have probably benefitted from the increasing area under agriculture.

Past and current management Because of its habit of disrupting the surface of fields, the mole has historically been persecuted, and can still legally be trapped. Their excavations are a particular problem in relation to silage making, where the presence of soil can spoil the fermentation process. There are still some professional mole-catchers working in Highland, and a row of dead moles hanging on a fence, to demonstrate success, has been seen as recently as 2010. Various sonic devices and vibrating windmills are available, claiming to repel moles from domestic lawns, but their efficacy is doubtful. The recent arrival of the New Zealand flatworm, which feeds on earthworms, may threaten the continued existence of moles in areas where it establishes.

Current distribution Found wherever soils are deep and free-draining enough to support earthworms. Mole hills are most commonly seen in grassland and arable fields in the lower-lying farmed and crofted areas of the Highland mainland. Apparently isolated groups of mole hills may be encountered where suitable soils occur at higher altitudes in the hills, among bog or moorland vegetation, and also on islands in rivers. Whether these represent persistent populations of moles, or just transient individuals, is a mystery. The mole is said to have been introduced to Skye, and occurs on Isle Ristol in Loch Broom, but appears to be absent (or perhaps just unrecorded?) from other Highland islands.

Nature of records The vast majority of records (94%) are of mole hills, but cat kills, moles trapped deliberately, moles found dead (including roadkill) and live sightings are also recorded.

Distributional trends Recorded from 188 Highland 10km squares in the 1993 Atlas compared to 216 now. This slight increase is probably due to increased recording effort.

Where to look Moles are very difficult to see and even watching an actively-growing molehill rarely reveals a glimpse of the perpetrator.

Mole   Grey dot = 1999 and before   Black dot = 2000 and after

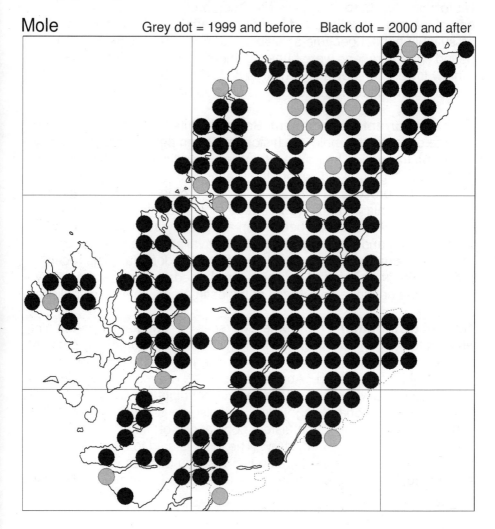

48

Common shrew

Sorex araneus Linnaeus, 1758

Order: Soricomorpha

Gaelic: dallag-fhraoich

Conservation status W&C Act Schedule 6 (need a licence to live-trap)

Recognition and signs Despite its name, not necessarily the commonest shrew in all Highland habitats. Smaller than a mouse and very active. A member of the insectivore family, with a long mobile snout, barely perceptible eyes and small teeth. The tail is 50-60% of the combined head and body length (compared to 70% in the pygmy shrew). Total length 70-120mm. It short, dense fur is brown on top and grey beneath, with a band of pale brown in between. Shrews can change size throughout the year, becoming smaller in winter through shrinkage of the skeleton and some organs. This reduces their overall energy requirement. Weights vary from 5-14g. Reliable methods of identification are: skull remains found in raptor or owl pellets or discarded bottles or cans (teeth are different from pygmy shrew); live-trapping; live sightings (if you get a good look); and dead carcases.

Ecology and behaviour Found in a variety of habitats, wherever vegetation provides enough cover to hide them in runs and burrows; rank grassland, scrub, woodland, roadside verges, field margins, moorland and rocky screes. Spends more time below ground than the pygmy shrew. Feeds on invertebrates of all shapes and sizes - earthworms, slugs, snails, beetles, spiders, woodlice, springtails and insect larvae, but takes a greater proportion of underground prey (e.g. earthworms) than either the pygmy or water shrew. Common shrews are largely solitary and keep apart from each other except when mating. Encounters usually result in aggression. Individual home ranges are of the order of a few hundred square metres (no data from Highland). Common shrews are active in short bursts of 1-2 hours duration throughout the day and night, and must consume 80-90% of their body weight daily to meet their energy needs. Nests, of dried grasses and leaves, are made above or below ground in secure locations. Breeding takes place from May to August, after which the breeding adults die. Only the young overwinter to produce next year's breeding population. A female can have between 2 and 5 litters of 4-8 young in a season. Young are born after a gestation of 20 days, and suckled for 22-25 days before weaning. One litter can contain young fathered by several different males, who play no further part in rearing them. Shrews are preyed upon by raptors and owls (most frequently barn owls), but mammalian predators seem to find them distasteful and often don't eat those they have killed.

History in Highland Recent genetic work (Searle *et al.,* 2009) shows that Common shrews are one of the small mammals with a 'Celtic fringe' in the British Isles. Those in northern Scotland are genetically more similar to those in Wales and Cornwall than to those in most of England. They possibly represent a survival from the first wave of colonists after the last glaciation, which were replaced in the south by later waves of immigrants. Historical observers failed to distinguish between common and pygmy shrews, or indeed between shrews and mice, so it is difficult to be certain about early records. Pennant (1777) reports only one kind of shrew, the "Foetid shrew" or "Dallag an fhraoich", presumably the common shrew. The faunas describe them as 'common' or 'abundant' on the mainland.

Past and current management Not being particularly troublesome to humans, common shrews are largely left to their own devices.

Current distribution Widely distributed across the Highland mainland but under-recorded. Of the islands, present only on Skye, Raasay, Scalpay and Soay. Also reported from Rona, Eigg and the Crowlins by Berry (1983). One was trapped in a rat trap on Eigg in 1992, but further evidence is needed to ascertain whether this represents an established population, rather than a casual arrival via human or raptor.

Nature of records Two-thirds of records are of cat kills or shrews found dead, with the remaining third divided between live-trap records, live sightings and identification from skeletal remains in owl or raptor pellets and bottles or cans.

Distributional trends Recorded in 106 10km squares in the ITE Atlas 1993 and 91 now. Both probably represent under-recording.

Where to look Difficult to predict where common shrews may be seen scurrying about above ground. More frequently their high-pitched squeaks can be heard emanating from vegetation cover, by those with good high-range hearing.

Fascinating fact In his articles on the Quadrupeds of Caithness (1862-3) in the John O'Groat Journal (Clark & Sellers, 2005), Robert Shearer reported that the common shrew was known as "shear mouse" and thought by country people to be fatally poisonous if handled. This is of course untrue!

Common shrew

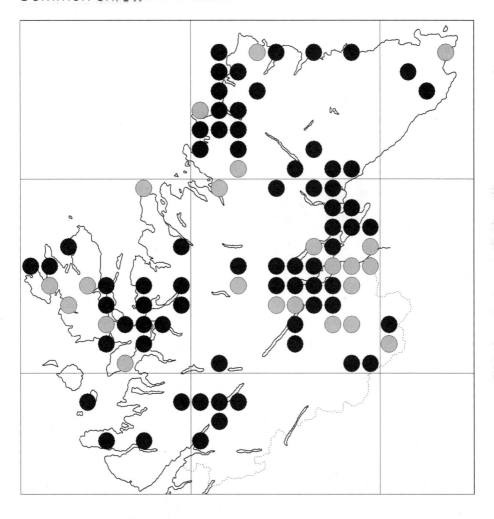

Grey dot = 1999 and before
Black dot = 2000 and after

Pygmy shrew
Sorex minutus Linnaeus, 1766

Order: Soricomorpha
Gaelic: fionnag-feòir

Conservation status W&C Act Schedule 6 (need a licence to live-trap)

Recognition and signs Britain's smallest non-flying mammal, and commoner than the common shrew in some habitats. Generally smaller than common shrew, (although there is some size overlap), with a thicker and more densely-furred tail. The tail is about 70% of the combined head and body length (compared to 50-60% in the common shrew). Pelage is brown on top and grey beneath, lacking the three-colour stripe of the common shrew. Total length 70-100mm; weight 2.5-6g. There are differences in the teeth which make it possible to differentiate between common and pygmy shrews from skulls found in owl pellets. Otherwise they are difficult to tell apart except in the hand, after live-trapping or being found dead. Shrews lead a fast-paced lifestyle, are short-lived and so are quite often found just lying dead on the ground.

Ecology and behaviour The pygmy shrew lives in a wide variety of habitats, wherever there is dense vegetation cover. It spends more time above ground than the common shrew, and is more abundant in moorland and blanket bog habitats. It achieves higher population densities in grassland than in woodland. Pygmy shrews find most of their prey on the ground surface, and mainly take invertebrates less than 10mm in length (i.e. not the big earthworms taken by common shrews). They will eat beetles, woodlice, flies, spiders, harvestmen, insect larvae and occasionally small slugs and snails. Pygmy shrews have a higher metabolic rate than common shrews, and need to eat more than their own body weight of prey per day. Perhaps because of this, their home range sizes can be larger than those of the common shrew, ranging from 200 to 1800m^2 (no data from Highland). Pygmy shrews are reported to make less noise than common shrews - or is it that their vocalisations are too high-pitched for us to hear?
Breeding takes place from May to August, after which the breeding adults die. Only the young overwinter to produce next year's breeding population. A female can have several litters of 4-6 young in a season. Young are born after a gestation of 20-25 days, and weigh only ¼g at birth. They are suckled for 22 days before weaning. The pygmy shrew's main predators are owls, kestrels and buzzards. Mammalian

predators tend to kill but not to eat them, presumably because they taste bad.

History in Highland Pygmy shrews are one of the 'Celtic fringe' mammals (Searle et al., 2009). Those from the western Highlands and islands are genetically different from those in the eastern Highlands and England. The two types are thought to result from different waves of colonisation following the ice age. Their more recent history in Highland is confused by the lack of recognition of different shrew species by early naturalists. Harvie-Brown (1895) reports them as "only recently recognised as occurring".

Past and current management The existence of pygmy shrews passes largely beneath the human radar and they are left to their own devices.

Current distribution Widely distributed across the Highland mainland, but under-recorded. Recorded from more islands than the common shrew (possibly because they are better able to survive boat-travel?): Rum, Canna, Eigg, Muck, Skye, Raasay, Pabay, Soay and Handa. Also reported from Rona and Scalpay by Berry (1983) but we have no records.

Nature of records Two-thirds of records are either cat kills or animals found dead. The remaining third comprise live trappings and sightings, plus skulls from owl pellets.

Distributional trends Recorded from similar numbers (50+) of 10km squares in the ITE Atlas and now. Both probably represent serious under-recording.

Where to look Shrews may occasionally be observed on the ground surface scurrying about, but they won't stay still long enough for you to be able to tell which species.

Fascinating fact Baby pygmy shrews have a phenomenal growth rate, multiplying their birth weight tenfold in 14 days.

Pygmy shrew

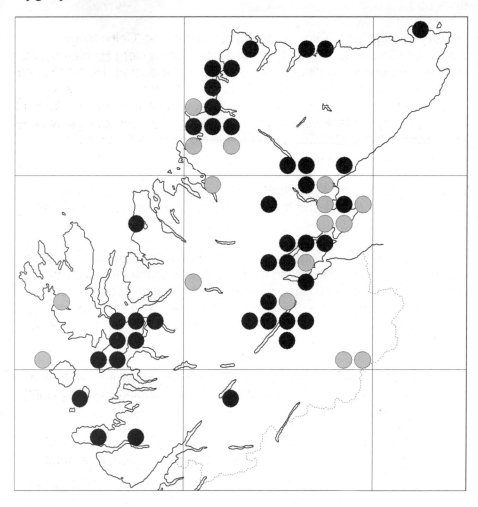

Grey dot = 1999 and before
Black dot = 2000 and after

Water shrew

Neomys fodiens (Pennant, 1771)
Synonym: Eurasian water shrew

Order: Soricomorpha
Gaelic: dallag-uisge

Conservation status W&C Act Schedule 6 (need a licence to live-trap)

Recognition and signs Britain's only aquatic shrew. It is larger in size than the common shrew and has a distinctive two-tone pelage, being black on top and white beneath. Adapted for an aquatic lifestyle by having a row of stiff hairs, along the outer edges of its feet and under the tail, which assist with swimming. Its long whiskers are thought to be used to detect prey. Length 110-170mm. Weight 12-18g. Like the common shrew, it may reduce its size in winter. Its presence can be confirmed by analysis of droppings left in bait tubes. Plastic tubes baited with mealworms, and with one end closed off, are placed in appropriate habitat. The bait encourages any passing shrew to stay in the tube long enough to deposit droppings. These can then be analysed, and if aquatic invertebrate remains are found, indicate that they were left by a water shrew. Its distinctive teeth mean that skulls can be identified from owl pellets.

Ecology and behaviour Lives in small unpolluted streams and water bodies, and occasionally garden ponds. It feeds on aquatic invertebrates such as water slaters, shrimps, caddis fly larvae, amphibians, fish and snails. Water shrews can live on terrestrial prey if they have to. Has also been seen foraging on the sea shore, but presumably for sand hoppers along the strand line, rather than in the sea itself. Water shrews produce a venom in their saliva which helps them to subdue prey larger than themselves. Their bite causes irritation to human skin, but nothing serious. They live in small-diameter (2cm) burrows at the water's edge, or in old bank vole or wood mouse burrows. Home ranges (no data from Highland) can be from 60-500m^2 in streamside habitats, and appear to be transitory. Water shrews can dive to about 2m and remain submerged for up to 24s. They need to consume 50% of their body weight daily. Their nests of dried grass, moss and leaves are usually made below ground. Breeding takes place from May to August, and each female can have 1 or 2 litters per breeding season. Gestation lasts 19-21 days, and litters can contain as many as 15 young, but usually consist of about 6. They are suckled for 38-40 days and leave their mother once weaned. Most adult water shrews die at the end of the breeding season, with only the young overwintering to breed the following year. The water shrew's main predators are owls, kestrels and buzzards, but they may occasionally be eaten by mammals or large fish.

History in Highland The water shrew's occurrence in the limestone burns of Assynt is noted in the faunas. Robert Shearer (Clark & Saunders, 2005) said of it in Caithness "Not so abundant as the Common shrew, but by no means scarce. The same popular beliefs hold good regarding this shrew as regarding the other, only, I believe, that this one is considered much more hurtful than any other animal."

Past and current management The existence of water shrews passes largely unnoticed and they are left to their own devices.

Current distribution Sparsely distributed on the mainland, and present on Skye, Raasay, Pabay and Isle Ristol.

Nature of records Just over half of records are either of live sightings or animals found dead. Some records come from the Mammal Society's Water Shrew survey of 2004 to 2005 (Carter & Churchfield, 2006).

Distributional trends Recorded in 31 10km squares in ITE Atlas and 59 now. No trend apparent, but probably under-recorded in both cases.

Where to look Extremely difficult to see unless you happen to be lucky enough to have them move in to your garden pond.

Fascinating fact Recent research in Canada (Catania *et al.*, 2008) has shown that water shrews there (albeit of a different species *Sorex palustris*) are just as efficient at catching prey in the dark as in daylight. They respond to the movement of water indicating a fleeing target, feel for prey with their whiskers and can use their sense of smell under water by blowing bubbles out of their nose and breathing them back in again. It would be interesting to know whether our water shrews also do this.

Water shrew

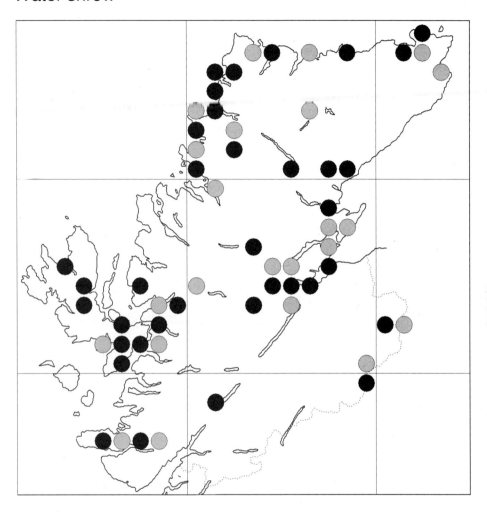

Grey dot = 1999 and before
Black dot = 2000 and after

Bats

Gaelic: ialtag (bat – whilst there are Gaelic names for different bat species, there is not yet a formally agreed naming system)

This introductory page covers aspects which are common to the seven species of bats which have been recorded in Highland.

Conservation status EHD Annex IV (EPS); SBL; all except Daubenton's bat, Natterer's bat and Nathusius' pipistrelle are also on the UKBAP list.

Recognition Bat calls as heard though a bat detector can be heard at: http://www.bats.org.uk/pages/bat_sound_library.html.

Past and current management Before bats were protected, past management may have consisted of eviction (deliberately or inadvertently) from buildings and structures where they were roosting. Their current fully protected status means that this should no longer happen. Licences can be issued to allow activities which would otherwise be offences to take place in a controlled and specified manner. This often includes mitigation such as carrying out the operation at a specific time of year, to reduce adverse impacts on bats. Scottish Natural Heritage (SNH) provides advice to people who may be concerned about bats within or affecting their property. Where proposed operations or works (whether by the public, developers, businesses, local councils or utility companies) will impact upon bats, the services of a professional bat consultant should be sought.

Nature of records Due to their nocturnal habits and difficulties of identification, most bat records come either from licence-holders who are able to identify bats in the hand, or are identified from their calls using a bat detector, either at roost counts, or whilst out foraging. With the legal requirement for Environmental Impact Assessments covering protected species to be undertaken prior to developments such as wind farms, increasing numbers of targeted bat surveys are being carried out. It is hoped that environmental consultants will follow the advice of the Institute of Ecology and Environmental Management (IEEM, 2009) and submit their data to appropriate national and local recording schemes, including HBRG.

Daubenton's bat

Myotis daubentonii (Kuhl, 1817)

Order: Chiroptera

Alternative name: water bat

Recognition and signs Daubenton's bat is a small bat with short ears, brown (brown-grey), darkly bronze or with reddish tinged dorsal fur. The light grey, to whitish grey underparts are clearly delineated from the upperparts. Face colour is generally reddish brown; ears are brown, being slightly paler inside. The large feet are covered with long stiff bristles (Dietz *et al.*, 2009).
Daubenton's bat droppings can easily be confused with those of brown long-eared bat as they are of similar size and twisty in shape. Experience of both species is required to allow a confident identification. *Myotis* bats give audibly distinctive calls on a bat detector best heard at 45kHz, and described (for Daubenton's bat) as strong, fast, 'dry' clicks, the pulse repetition increasing the closer they get to their prey (Briggs & King, 1998). This is a fast and agile foraging species, often flying very low over the surface of water, patrolling back and forth over a favoured stretch of slack freshwater. This behaviour may aid in field identification, combined with ultrasonic calls heard on a bat detector. The *Myotis* group of bats can be difficult to distinguish from each other by call alone. Hence, good views or photographs (or a dead animal) are often required to distinguish between them. Of the *Myotis* species, only Daubenton's and Natterer's bat (*M. nattereri*) have so far been recorded in Highland (Battersby *et al.*, 2005; Richardson, 2000).

Ecology and behaviour Daubenton's bat is strongly associated with water, and will normally roost close to, and forage over, lochs and rivers (Racey *et al.*, 2004). It habitually hunts very low over water; ponds, lochs and smooth water surfaces of rivers and streams. It will take insects almost exclusively within 1m of the water surface and will often glean prey from the water surface. However, it will also occasionally forage within woodland (Altringham, 2003). Its prey consists mainly of aquatic flies; midges, caddis flies, mosquitoes, mayflies and lacewings. Highland breeding roost locations include a wide range of sites including mature trees, derelict buildings, castles, bridges, and some maternity roosts have been found in houses (Racey *et al.,* 2004). The behaviour of roosting within houses is mainly restricted to Scotland and may be linked to temperature requirements for breeding. In common with most bat species, they generally use the same roost sites

from year to year, but may move between a range of different roost sites within a given year.
Daubenton's bat will hibernate in a range of habitats, preferring a stable cool environment, often underground, using caves, mines and lime-kilns (Racey *et al.*, 2004). Ice-houses are also used if environmental conditions (i.e. high humidity and stable low temperatures) are suitable (authors' obs.) There are no records yet of this species hibernating within buildings in Scotland (Racey *et al.*, 2004).

History in Highland Daubenton's bat was recorded as common in various Scottish localities, being noted as far north as the River Spey (Thorburn, 1974). There is little other information on the historical status of this species from Highland. Only two records of this species in Highland were recorded from 1980-1991 (Haddow, 1992).

Current distribution Foraging records are widely distributed within Highland, although there are gaps in North Sutherland and on the west coast (north of Fort William) where this species has yet to be recorded (although there is one past observation on Skye). Confirmation of Daubenton's bat in NW Sutherland (at Ullapool NH19, Lochinver NH02 and Scourie NH14) suggests that a lack of records in West Highland could be attributable to low survey effort, as some habitats appear suitable for foraging. Notably, a Daubenton's roost site has been recorded from West Highland, near Kyle of Lochalsh NG72 (Richardson, 2000). However, brown long-eared bat (a true nocturnal species – similar to Daubenton's bat) has been well recorded from West Highland. So further survey effort for Daubenton's bat in West Highland would help clarify this situation.
Dingwall and Inverness areas support a cluster of confirmed sightings. Records from Caithness indicate that this species could be recorded close to the very north coast of Scotland, if suitable habitat allows.

Distributional trends Daubenton's bat was recorded in ten 10km squares within Highland in the ITE Atlas, compared to over 60 now. The geographical spread of the earlier records is generally similar to the current distribution, and so the increase probably reflects increased recording effort rather than range expansion.

Where to look Observations (aided with a bat detector) adjacent to sheltered rivers or lochs should pick-up calls of foraging Daubenton's bat. Bridges allow good observations of bats foraging on rivers below.

Fascinating fact Although this species is wide spread over Highland, systematic bat survey work on bridges in East Sutherland found that it comprised only 11% of the foraging bat assemblage. No Daubenton's roost sites were discovered in bridges surveyed (Wells & Patterson, 2005). However, roost sites of this species were discovered in road bridges at Gairlochy (NN18) and Fort Augustus (NH30) in the early 1990s (Whitaker, 1995).

Daubenton's bat

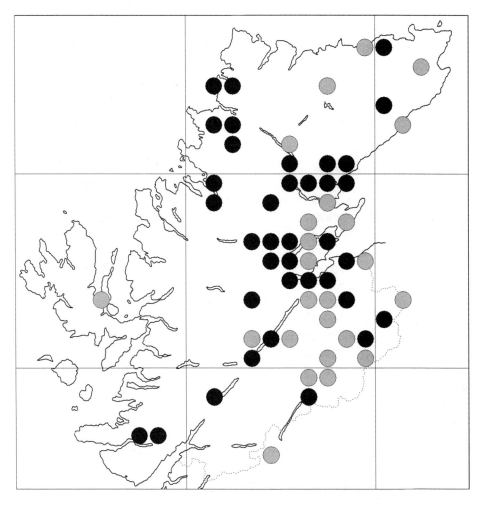

Grey dot = 1999 and before   Black dot = 2000 and after

Natterer's bat

Order: Chiroptera

Myotis nattereri (Kuhl 1817)

Synonym: red-armed bat

Recognition and signs A medium sized bat with long, shaggy fur, light brown on upper side and pale buff to white underside. Easily distinguished in the hand by the stiff hairs fringing the tail membrane. Also a distinctive backwards flick to the tips of the large ears and a long, narrow, pointed tragus which is 3/4 of the ear length. The muzzle is pink and balding as are the limbs giving rise to its old name of 'red armed' bat. Calls of the two *Myotis* species are difficult to differentiate, but Natterer's rapid 'clicks' are less regular than Daubenton's calls and sound like 'stubble burning'. Natterer's bat droppings are about 2.3-3.3mm in diameter and about 8-11mm in length with medium particle size and an irregular shape. Natterer's fly with a slow, agile flight at head height along habitat edges, catching insects on the wing within 2-5 cm of vegetation – a feat not seen in any other bat. Flight is faster and more direct when commuting from roost to foraging site.

Ecology and behaviour Natterer's have a varied insectivorous diet including flies, moths, beetles, caddis flies and frequently spiders. They mainly hawk insects (catch and eat them on the wing) but will also glean insects off foliage, including grass. Gleaning bats have the advantage that they do not have to rely on the post-dusk and pre-dawn aerial insect peaks and are less dependent on air temperature as they can still get prey when insects are not flying. Woodland habitat is preferred, varying from dense woodland, including conifer plantations, to gardens and open parks for feeding. They also forage low over water.
Summer roosts are found trees including split conifer trees. Timber and stone buildings are also used and bat boxes including for maternity roosts. Maternity roosts can contain 30 to 200 bats but males can make up to 25% of the colony. Summer male-only colonies of up to 30 individuals have been recorded. Most Natterer's are faithful to a small number of roost sites. Hibernation sites are almost exclusively mines and tunnels with the bats found mainly in cracks and crevices.

History in Highland No specific historical records are known.

Current distribution Resident only in southern Highland – no roosts have been recorded north of Inverness. The most northerly individual Natterer's recorded in Britain are those from NH18 and NH78.

Distributional trends Natterer's bat was recorded from five 10km squares in the ITE Atlas, compared to 17 now. This may reflect increased recording effort and/or some northern range expansion.

Where to look Most likely to be seen in southern Highland, near woodland and water on a calm, warm evening with a bat detector tuned to 50 kHz. Worth trying new places, as it's probably under-recorded.

Fascinating fact Several records are of individuals found dead on the road, including one found on a car radiator grille. This unfortunate situation is probably due to their low flying behaviour.

Natterer's bat   Grey dot = 1999 and before   Black dot = 2000 and after

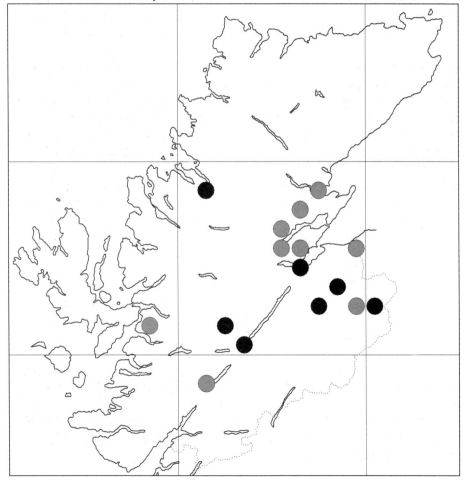

Noctule

Nyctalus noctula (Schreber 1774)

Recognition and signs One of Britain's largest bats, with a wingspan of 320-450mm. In the hand it has sleek fur, golden, reddish or chocolate brown, uniform in colour from tip to base and slightly paler on the underside. The ears are short and broad with a distinct mushroom shaped tragus. Often emerging early in the evening, it has distinctive long, narrow, pointed wings. It is a high, fast flier with a straight flight pattern that is interrupted with steep dives when hunting. Echolocation calls are very loud, slow, irregular and heard on a bat detector as a chip-chop or as metallic chinks. Almost exclusively it roosts in tree holes, which can be recognised by black streaks of faeces and urine draining from the exit hole. Droppings are 11-15mm long, 3-3.5mm wide. Roosts can also be revealed by audible shrill calls near dusk.

Ecology and behaviour The noctule feeds in the open for about an hour just after dusk and just before dawn. Usually seen above trees and water, they eat mainly large prey on the wing; flies, moths, beetles and crickets. From roost to foraging site they may commute up to 10km. Roosts are usually in rot holes and woodpecker holes in trees, rarely in bat boxes and buildings. Nursery roosts in Britain rarely exceed 20 individual females. Males in summer are solitary or form a small group and in August and September set up territorial mating roosts which the females visit. For hibernation, trees are mainly used although they have been recorded in buildings and occasionally caves. In Eastern Europe noctules will migrate 2,000km to hibernate but in Britain they are thought to either be non-migratory or travel shorter distances.

History in Highland There are no specific historical records of noctule in Highland, although Inverness Museum holds a record of one being shot in Nairn in the early 1900s.

Current distribution The noctule is a rare visitor to Highland. Single individuals have been recorded only three times since 2000; one in NC50 (May 2000), and two in NH45 (August 2005 and October 2006). Unidentified 'large bats' have also been seen in Skye (NG42 and NG61) in October 1993 and August 2011 and at Laxford Bridge, Sutherland (NC24) in October 1993.

Distributional trends There were no noctule records from Highland in the ITE atlas. Its status as a rare visitor this far north has not changed.

Where to look The noctule has a very loud echolocation call and, being an early emerger at dusk, it can easily be seen and heard where it is present. In Highland the records are so infrequent that luck is probably your best ally.

Noctule

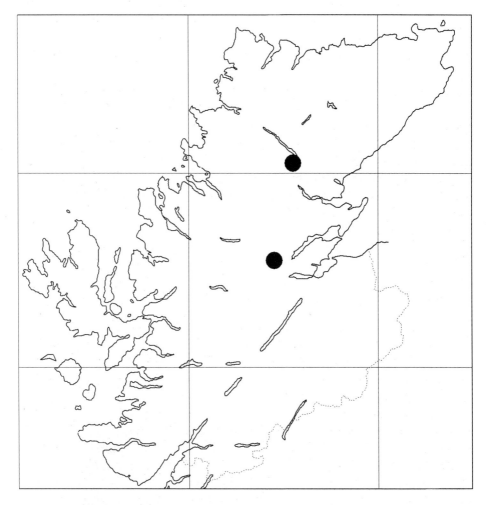

Grey dot = 1999 and before   Black dot = 2000 and after

Common pipistrelle

Order: Chiroptera

Pipistrellus pipistrellus (Schreber, 1774)
Previous name: bandit pipistrelle, pipistrelle bat

Recognition and signs A small brown-coloured bat with small triangular ears; its upper parts are dark-brown (reddish-brown), with paler yellow-brown underparts (sometimes grey-brown). Dark (black-brown) ears and a dark coloured face give this species a dark, almost bandit type mask (Dietz *et al.*, 2009). Droppings are small and mouse-like, often sticking to gable walls and windows, which give away the presence of a bat roost.

This species often utilises the outer fabric of buildings (i.e. under slates, ridge tiles, chimney flashings and above wall-heads, etc), and as a result their presence can often go unnoticed by home owners for many years. However, common pipistrelle can sometimes be heard softly squeaking and chittering on hot days (especially close to dusk). This bat echolocates prey and identification is possible with the use of an ultra-sonic bat detector. Common pipistrelles emit their peak 'wet' smack repetitive calls at around 45 kHz (Briggs and King, 1998). Common and Soprano pipistrelle were considered to be the same species (i.e. Pipistrelle bat) until they were proved to be distinctly separate as recently as 1995 (Racey *et al.*, 2004).

Ecology and behaviour The pipistrelle is an insectivore, feeding on a variety of small flying insects (e.g. small flies, caddisflies, mayflies, lacewings and moths, etc), securing their prey on the wing. Favoured foraging habitats include; slow moving rivers, lochs, mature woodland, woodland edge, hedgerows, churchyards and large gardens. However, common pipistrelles in Highland are also known to forage and roost in upland habitats (authors' obs.) usually thought to be avoided by bats. In addition, radio telemetry studies in North Sutherland have shown common pipistrelle to fly >7km to forage along sheltered coastal cliff grasslands, with one individual flying *c.*2km over the sea to return to the roost site before dawn (authors' obs.). These reports suggest that Highland common pipistrelles are relatively hardy animals, utilising a range of marginal habitats and subsisting within remote harsh environments, ensuring their successful spread throughout the Highlands of Scotland.

Highland breeding roost sites for common pipistrelles may include; domestic dwellings (even new builds), schools, stately homes, estate lodges, listed buildings, mature trees and rock outcrops. As in other Scottish locations, common pipistrelles often utilise rising heat from artificial heat sources (e.g. boilers and hot water units) within buildings to aid development of the young.

Winter roost behaviour is still poorly understood. However, there are Scottish records of pipistrelles using cooler parts of buildings during winter hibernation and torpor periods (e.g. November – March) (Racey et al., 2004). For example, at one site in Sutherland, common pipistrelles are strongly suspected to hibernate under lead roof flashing of a community hall clock tower, as bats have been observed swarming around the tower on the first warm night of the winter, in February (authors' obs.). Dedicated bat survey work at Assynt Caves (NC22) has found common pipistrelle to be frequenting upland open moorland close to the caves, but no evidence has yet been found that these caves are being used as roost sites (Wells, 2010). Coastal sea caves may also offer pipistrelles a possible hibernation site within Highland, as has been observed in at least one Scottish locality (Mortimer, 1995). In addition, pipistrelle bat species (most likely to be common pipistrelle) have been reported roosting within a sea cave on Handa Island.

History in Highland There appears minimal information on the historical status of this species within Highland. It was considered to be 'plentiful throughout the British Isles occurring in Scotland as far north as Orkney' (Thorburn, 1974).

Current distribution Common pipistrelle is the most numerous and widespread bat species in Highland. It has been recorded from all districts within Highland including outlying islands, such as Canna (Yoxon, 1993) and as far north as Bettyhill (NC76) and John O'Groat's (ND37) indicating the extent of its northern range. Thus the lack of records within central North Sutherland is likely to be due to the lack of recording effort for specific pipistrelle species.

Due to its apparent adaptability at utilising a range of habitats, including marginal upland habitats, coastal cliffs, etc, the common pipistrelle has succeeded in inhabiting some of the most unlikely Highland sites (see Ecology and Behaviour section). Although not recognised as a migrant species, small numbers of common pipistrelle have been recorded on offshore oil platforms in the North Sea during August and September (Thorpe, 2001). It is possible that transient individuals may contribute to Highland sightings of this species in very remote locations, and may even help to repopulate the species at the north of its range should it experience decline.

Distributional trends Pipistrelle bat (undifferentiated) was recorded in 72 10km squares in the ITE Atlas. Since this time, the split of pipistrelle into two species confuses changes to the distribution of either. Common pipistrelle has now been recorded from 88 Highland 10km squares.
The extent of the distribution of the undifferentiated Pipistrelle records is generally similar to the extent of the current distribution within Highland. Thus, it is not considered that this species has markedly changed its distribution within the last 20+ years.

Where to look Common pipistrelles are generally widespread throughout Highland during the spring, summer and autumn. They can normally be seen just about anywhere, especially places which support sheltered woodland and scrub habitats with large areas of slow moving freshwater (e.g. lochs or rivers) where flying insects will be present in abundance. A bat detector will aid your enjoyment and understanding of these fascinating flying mammals.

Fascinating fact Two bat surveys recording the number of foraging bats around bridges and within pine woodland found that common pipistrelle accounted for 78% and 85% of the total bat foraging assemblage respectively (Wells & Patterson, 2005; Patterson & Wells, 2008). These surveys show that frequency of common pipistrelle is high within North Highland, as a proportion of the total bat assemblage. In addition, the above bat surveys cumulatively found that, of the two pipistrelle species foraging within East Sutherland, common pipistrelle comprised 92.5%, compared to soprano pipistrelle which only accounted for 7.5%.

Common pipistrelle

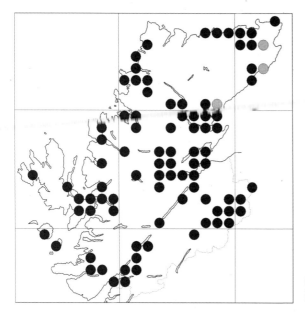

Grey dot = 1999 and before
Black dot = 2000 and after

Undifferentiated pipistrelle

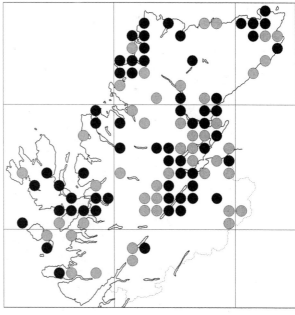

Soprano pipistrelle
Pipistrellus pygmaeus (Leach, 1825)

Order: Chiroptera
Previous name: pipistrelle bat

Recognition and signs A small bat, with short pale snout, strongly curved forehead and short pale ears. The light reddish brown fur of the upper parts is slightly paler on the underside giving this species a more two-tone colour appearance than common pipistrelle (Dietz *et al.* 2009). Soprano pipistrelle can generally be told apart from common pipistrelle by different colour of face parts and pelage.

This species can often be found within domestic property (i.e. attic spaces), but will also use the outer fabric of buildings (i.e. under slates, ridge tiles, chimney flashings and above wall-heads, etc). Soprano pipistrelle echolocates prey and identification is possible with the use of an ultra-sonic bat detector. Soprano pipistrelles emit their peak 'wet' repetitive smack echolocation calls at around 55 kHz (Briggs and King, 1998). Soprano pipistrelle and common pipistrelle were considered to be the same species (i.e. Pipistrelle bat) until they were proved to be distinctly separate as recently as 1995 (Racey *et al.*, 2004).

Ecology and behaviour The diet of soprano pipistrelle is more restricted than that of common pipistrelle (reflecting the soprano's specific habitat preference) feeding mainly on chironomid midges (Barlow, 1997). It finds its favoured forage in proximity of lowland valleys with abundant riparian vegetation (Swift, *et al.* 2001). As a high proportion of Highland supports marginal upland and true upland habitats, this could be a limiting factor in the soprano pipistrelle's distribution here.

In general, soprano pipistrelles roost communally, with females creating large maternity roosts during the summer breeding season (May-July) in Scotland. Mean colony size is 237 for soprano in Perth.& Kinross (Swift *et al.*, 2001). Maternity roosts often create problems with unsympathetic householders, as colonies of soprano pipistrelle tend to be larger and more odorous than roosts of common pipistrelle (Harris & Yalden, 2008).

Highland breeding roosts may include a wide range of sites including; domestic dwellings, schools, stately homes, estate lodges, listed buildings and mature trees, etc. Heat is important for the success of maternity roosts either naturally from a south facing aspect, or as artificial heat from buildings. Soprano pipistrelle is considered more faithful (than common pipistrelle) to one roost site during the breeding

period (Racey *et al.,* 2004). In common with most bat species, they generally use the same roost sites from year to year.
Winter roost behaviour is still poorly understood. However, there are Scottish records of pipistrelles using cooler parts of buildings during winter hibernation and torpor periods (e.g. November – March). Therefore, it is possible that pipistrelles often hibernate in crevices within unheated parts of buildings and may stay close to their summer roost sites (Racey *et al.,* 2004).

History in Highland Because of the recent recognition of soprano pipistrelle as a separate species, there is no historical information on its distribution. Baseline data published in this Atlas will help discern any future change in distribution.

Current distribution The soprano pipistrelle is less frequently recorded than the common pipistrelle. There is a thin scattering of records from the west coast, with only six from Skye north to Sutherland. Small clusters of records are present from more urban areas of Inverness (NH64) and Dingwall (NH55). Another cluster is present in south-east Sutherland where intensive bat surveys have been completed in the recent past. There are a few records north of Lairg (NC50), which includes two from Lochinver (NC02) and Caithness. Thus, this species is present within Highland but appears to be 'uncommon' further north within Sutherland and Caithness (Patterson & Wells, 2008). Harris & Yalden (2008), classify soprano pipistrelle as 'scarce' within North Sutherland and Caithness. Further recording effort is required to accurately map Soprano pipistrelle and assess its distribution and frequency at its northern limit within Highland. No maternity roosts of soprano pipistrelle have yet been recorded from North Highland, although a roost (status unknown) is suspected at Lairg (NC50) (authors' obs.).
As all maternity roosts assessed within North Highland by SNH bat workers have been common pipistrelle (thus far), and bearing in mind that soprano pipistrelle often provoke more concern from roost owners than other bat species (as they are usually more odorous), it can be deduced that soprano pipistrelle does not have the large roosts in Highland that it enjoys within central and southern Scotland (authors' obs.). As the species is clearly present within Highland, it either has small maternity roosts that go unnoticed by householders, or it shares roosts with other bat species where it may be difficult to detect even by bat surveyors. Soprano pipistrelle has been known to join Daubenton's

bat roosts in Scotland (J. Haddow *pers. comm.*) but roost sharing with other bat species has yet to be fully documented within Highland.

Distributional trends Pipistrelle bat (undifferentiated) was recorded in 72 10km squares in the ITE Atlas. Since its recognition as a separate species, the soprano pipistrelle has been recorded in just over 40 Highland 10km squares. Records appear less frequent in the north, perhaps reflecting a northern limit to their distribution.

Where to look Research work within Scotland has shown that the soprano pipistrelle favours riparian habitats, often associated with large slow moving rivers or large lochs with abundant waterside vegetation. Therefore, sampling this habitat with a bat detector will increase your chances of picking up a soprano pipistrelle.

Fascinating fact Other surveys have shown that soprano pipistrelle is more common further south within Scotland. In Perth & Kinross and Clackmannanshire both pipistrelle species were found to be equally abundant (Swift *et al.*, 2001). Two foraging bat surveys in East Sutherland found that of the two pipistrelle species, common accounted for 92.5% of passes, compared to only 7.5% for soprano (Wells & Patterson, 2005; Patterson & Wells, 2008). Dedicated bat survey transects by car, covering large areas of the region, may help to increase our understanding of the distribution of this species within Highland.

Nathusius' pipistrelle

Order: Chiroptera

Pipistrellus nathusii (Keyserling & Blasius, 1839)

There has so far been only one authenticated record of Nathusius' pipistrelle in Highland, of three bats foraging together near Wick (NC35) in September 2010. This is a rare bat in Britain, with only four known maternity roosts (Harris & Yalden, 2008). It has been recorded in NE Scotland, and on North Sea oil platforms, so its occurrence here may be as a vagrant. Its main range is in eastern and central Europe.

Soprano pipistrelle

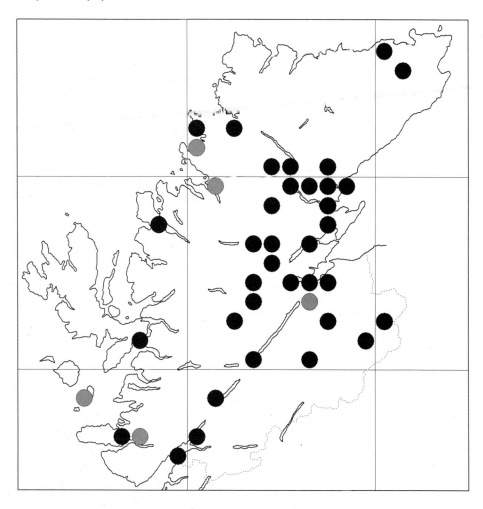

Grey dot = 1999 and before
Black dot = 2000 and after

Brown Long-eared Bat

Order: Chiroptera

Plecotus auritus (Linnaeus, 1758)

Recognition and signs A medium-sized bat with very long delicate ears, which are folded back under the wings when torpid. The long pointed tragus (inner ear-flap) projects forward even when the ears are folded. The upper body fur is brown, sometimes with a reddish tinge, blending gradually into the cream to yellowish-grey underparts. The face is usually light brown, comprising of a short muzzle. The eyes are large (compared to other British bats) and black (Dietz *et al.*, 2009). Droppings can be similar in size and shape to those of Daubenton's bat but can be differentiated with experience. Brown long-eared bats will often leave discarded moth wings below regularly used feeding/resting sites (Altringham, 2003). This, along with droppings, helps to support recognition of the species in Highland.

The brown long-eared bat is often called the 'whisperer bat' as calls are unusually quiet. Observations (aided by a moonlit night) of a medium sized bat flying within a woodland canopy registering only quiet or no calls on a bat detector can be a good indication of brown long-eared bat presence (Briggs & King, 1998). It is seldom confused with other bat species within Highland.

Ecology and behaviour The brown long-eared bat is strongly associated with tree cover and as a result will normally select roosts within 0.5km of broad-leaved woodland. This species prefers deciduous woodland as a foraging habitat but will also use mixed and conifer woodlands (Racey *et al.*, 2004). A bat survey of high quality Scots pine woodlands in East Sutherland found brown long-eared bats to be the second most numerous bat, with 51 bat passes comprising 6.5% of the total bat foraging assemblage (Patterson & Wells, 2008). The brown long-eared bat has short broad wings allowing for slow, manoeuvrable flight as it hawks for insects, often gleaning them from the surfaces of tree foliage. It will hover and use its long ears to listen for movement of its prey. Its large eyes may assist in detecting prey at close quarters. Moths comprise an important component of its diet (Altringham, 2003).

This species is closely associated with breeding in large attics of traditional old houses, although churches and farm steadings are also favoured. Further south, it has a reliance on tree holes as roost sites, perhaps indicating its preference for warmth from houses in Scotland to

Plate I

a. Red squirrel on nut feeder, Strathspey.
b. Spruce cones handled by red squirrel (above) and wood mouse (below).

c. Hazel nuts opened by wood mouse

d. Young wood mouse eating

e. Water vole feeding remains

f. Water vole latrine and burrow

Plate II

a. A long-standing otter spraint site on the west coast

b. American mink in a garden pond

c. Otter tracks, scrapes and spraint on sand

Plate III

a. Badger dung after mixed diet – fruit pips visible

b. Badger dung after eating earthworms - amorphous mass

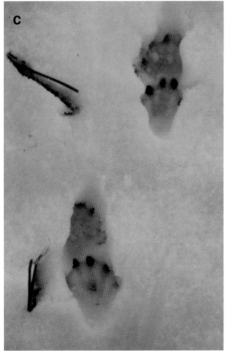

c. Otter tracks in snow – note five toes and webs between

d. Fox tracks in snow – note two middle claws parallel

Plate IV

a. Bearded seal seen in the Inverness Firth in November 2007

b. Badger fore footprint - note five toes with long claws

c. Rabbits - doe gathering nesting material

d. Roe buck with antlers in velvet

e. Red deer tracks in sand (going right > left) – note small dew claw impressions behind cleaves.

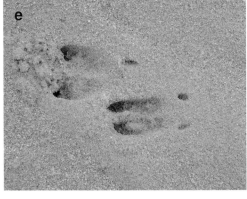

aid rearing of young (Racey *et al.*, 2004). In addition, it has also been found roosting in reasonable numbers (20+) within small buildings with low attic spaces of <1m internal height (authors' obs.).

Maternity roosts can sometimes create problems with householders, as attics are often occupied for protracted periods (i.e. March - November). In common with most bat species, they generally use the same roost sites from year to year.

Brown long-eared bats will hibernate in a range of different habitats, preferring a stable cool environment, often underground, using caves, and mines (Racey *et al* 2004). Ice-houses are also used if environmental conditions (i.e. stable low temperatures) are suitable (authors' obs.).

There are few reports of brown long-eared bats hibernating within buildings during the winter. However, there are reports of this species flying in very close proximity to domestic roost sites on warm winter nights in December and February (V. Wilson *pers. comm.*), perhaps indicating that some individuals may also use their favoured roost site during the winter.

History in Highland There appears little other information published on the historical status or distribution of this species from Highland. However, Robert Innes Shearer described what is very likely to be brown long-eared bat in Caithness back in 1862. He describes that it can be found suspended from the ceiling with its ears folded back by its sides (Clark & Sellars, 2005).

Current distribution The brown long-eared bat is common and widespread in Britain, occurring everywhere except mountainous regions in north and north-west Scotland (Swift, 1998). However, as this species can be difficult to detect, the brown long-eared bat has the potential to be overlooked and under-recorded within Highland away from known maternity roost sites.

The species is considered to be rather sedentary and non-migratory (Altringham, 2003). However, it is known to visit autumn swarming and mating sites (Racey *et al.*, 2004; Glover & Altringham, 2008) which may require some local or regional movement. Yet, regular foraging distribution from roost sites is considered to be only up to 1.5km (Altringham, 2003; Racey *et al.*, 2004).

The most northerly known maternity roost in Highland is currently at Brora (NC80), south-east Sutherland (*own obs.*). However, one roost has previously been recorded from Lairg (NC50) (October 1986) and small maternity roosts (25km west of Lairg), possibly slightly north of Brora, were recorded in bat boxes back in August 1991 (Canham, 1992). Other northern Highland records involve; a single roosting brown long-eared bat near Wick (ND35) in September 2010, one brown long-eared bat found dead by the roadside on 12 October 2010 north of Latheron (ND23) (M. Swanson *pers. comm.*), a brown long-eared bat roost (unknown status) recorded *c.* 5km north of Loch Shin (NC42), (April 1996) and another record from the Caithness coast at Reay (NC96) back in 1980. Thus far, limited but positive observations of this species' presence in Caithness may point to small marginal roosts (in proximity to suitable broad-leaved woodland habitat) being present, but largely going unnoticed.

The brown long-eared bat has been recorded from islands including Skye (Yoxon, 1992), and one record showing presence on the Isle of Eigg. However, west Highland records are generally scattered, with most of the brown long-eared sightings coming from the eastern part.

Distributional trends The brown long-eared bat was recorded in 11 Highland 10km squares in the ITE Atlas, compared to over 80 now. It is now known to be much more widely distributed than previously thought. There is still scope for further recording in the north and west, but relatively low numbers may mean that the brown long-eared bat ('the whisperer') will be difficult to detect.

Where to look Night time visits to wooded church yards (complete with bat detector [friend and garlic!]) or lanes with mature trees are likely to prove fruitful. Try watching street lights in the autumn adjacent to mature trees or woodland as brown long-eared bats will often swoop under the light beam time and time again, hawking on moths attracted to the lights.

Fascinating fact It seems that the brown long-eared bat may continue to go under-recorded within Highland as many high quality remote bat detectors struggle to register their quiet calls. Visual night-time observations backed up with a hand-held bat detector appears to be the most reliable method for distinguishing foraging animals at present. These factors, in combination with large numbers of Highland biting midges, may limit our knowledge on the true distribution of the brown long-eared bat.

Brown long-eared bat

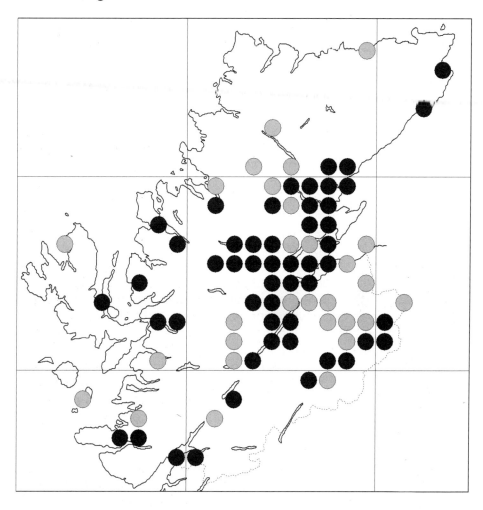

Grey dot = 1999 and before
Black dot = 2000 and after

Wildcat and feral cat

Order: Carnivora

Felis silvestris Schreber, 1777 (Wildcat)
Previous name: *Felis silvestris grampia*   Gaelic: cat fiadhaich
Felis catus, Felis silvestris catus (Domestic cat)   Gaelic: cat

Conservation status (Wildcat only) EHD Annex IV (EPS); W&C Act
Schedule 6; UKBAP; SBL; SNH SAF

Recognition and signs Distinguishing a wildcat from a tabby feral cat
is one of the most difficult challenges in Highland mammalogy. The two
are very closely related, (in fact current consensus is that they are sub-
species rather than full species) and can interbreed to produce fertile
offspring. Only in 2005 were reliable criteria devised for making the
distinction in a live specimen (Kitchener et al., 2005). Previous methods
had relied on differences in gut length, and the volume and morphology
of the skull – which are of only of use once the animal is dead. Wildcats
cannot be reliably identified in the field on the basis of size or behaviour.
Although wildcats are on average larger, heavier and more thick-set
than domestic/feral cats, there is a considerable overlap in size. Feral
cats can be just as fierce when cornered. The most frequently seen
part of a putative wildcat is the tail. If this is thick, with a blunt black tip
and separate black rings around it, with no vertical stripe joining them, it
is reasonable to suppose that what you have seen is a wildcat, provided
it meets the other criteria of being a stripy (not blotched) tabby, with no
large white patches. Signs such as droppings, footprints and scratch-
marks on trees cannot be allocated to either wildcat or feral cat, except
by habitat-based surmise.

Ecology and behaviour Originally (and across most of its present-day
European range) a woodland animal, the wildcat is now found also in
open habitats such as moorland, and in conifer plantations. Feral cats
tend to occur closer to human habitation. Both wild and feral cats prey
on small mammals, rabbits, birds, fish, amphibians and reptiles, and
sometimes carrion. Wildcat home range sizes vary considerably,
depending on habitat quality, but the only study so far carried out in
Highland found that they can be larger than 1,000ha on the west coast
(Scott, Easterbee and Jefferies 1992). Although often stated to be
crepuscular or nocturnal, wildcats can be active during daylight hours
when in thick cover (author's obs.). Female wildcats usually have only
one litter per year, but ferals, particularly those living in association with

humans, where food is plentiful, may have several. Wildcat litters consist of 1-3 kittens, whereas ferals may have more. Kittens are weaned at 6-7 weeks and fully independent at 5 months.

History in Highland Wildcats were formerly widespread, but had been persecuted almost to extinction by the end of the 19th century (Langley & Yalden, 1977). Their survival in the extreme north-west of Highland is more likely the due to the lower levels of persecution there, in the absence of grouse moors, rather than because the habitat was particularly favourable. Although now fully protected, their survival as a species is still at risk of 'genetic extinction' through interbreeding with domestic and feral cats. Recent apparent wildcat range expansion may have been achieved by inter-breeding. Almost nothing is known of the historical distribution of domestic cats, and hence feral cats, in Highland. Cats were first domesticated (from the closely-related African wildcat, *Felis silvestris lybica*), as long as 9,000 years ago, in the near east (Driscoll *et al.*, 2007). They are thought to have been brought to Britain in Iron Age or Roman times and so could have had 2,000 years to interbreed with their wild counterparts. Although perhaps in the past, when human population density was lower, their separate habitats may have allowed them to maintain genetic independence. Written accounts of the clearances mention cats fleeing burning buildings.

Past and current management In earlier times, management of the wildcat consisted largely of attempting to exterminate it because of its alleged depredations on game birds. Now that we are more enlightened about the role of predators in the ecosystem, and the wildcat is fully protected, management is directed at avoiding damage to its places of shelter, trying to minimise opportunities for interbreeding with domestic cats and reducing the risk of disease transmission to wildcats from the domestic cat population (Macdonald *et al.,* 2004). Since 2008 a project in the Cairngorms National Park has been focussing on: raising awareness of the wildcat and its problems; using camera traps to record (any kind of) cat presence; trapping and neutering feral cats; and encouraging the owners of domestic cats to have them neutered and vaccinated.
Provision of good quality habitat in areas remote from human influence (such as some of the new native woodland schemes) may favour the survival of wildcats.

Current distribution The wildcat is widely but sparsely distributed throughout mainland Highland but absent from all of the islands. (The post-2000 record from Eigg NM48 is of feral cat). It would be useful to have more records of free-living feral cat colonies where these exist in Highland. Berry (1983) reported feral cats from Skye and Raasay.

Nature of records Many (193) of the pre-1999 wildcat records are historical ones gleaned from the records of an Inverness taxidermy firm (McGhie, 2002). These are discounted from the statistics given below. Because of the difficulty of making a positive identification of wildcat, about one third of the records are from road casualties, or animals otherwise obtained dead, which can be inspected closely. Live sightings comprise the other two thirds, and have only been accepted as wildcat if they meet the minimum criteria outlined above.

Distributional trends The wildcat was recorded from 193 Highland 10km squares in the ITE Atlas (including one in Skye, which has since been removed from the records, presumably as erroneous). This included the results of a national survey carried out during 1983-87 (Easterbee, Hepburn & Jefferies 1991). Recent (post-2000) HBRG records of wildcats in Highland exist from only 17 10km squares. This reflects the difficulty of recording such an elusive species, but possibly also the dilution of true wildcats by interbreeding with domestics. For all 'other cats' in the same date class, the number of 10km squares is 24. A survey commissioned by SNH (Davis & Gray, 2010) includes all HBRG records which fall within the survey's date class of 2006-8.

Where to look Because the wildcat is such a shy and cryptically-coloured animal, it is one of the most difficult to see in the wild. Wildcats tend to emerge from cover as it gets dark, and return at first light in the morning. So perhaps waiting (preferably inside a vehicle or hide) where there is a good view of a long stretch of forest edge, at dusk or dawn, is your best bet. Alternatively, the Highland Wildlife Park has a breeding group of wildcats.

Fascinating fact Because of its ferocious reputation the wildcat was adopted as the mascot of the Clan Macpherson, whose motto is "touch not the cat bot a glove" (i.e. don't touch the cat without a glove).

Feral, hybrid and undifferentiated cat

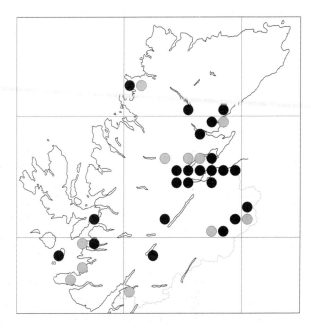

Wildcat

Grey dot = 1999 and before   Black dot = 2000 and after

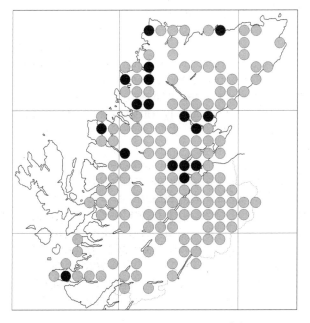

Fox

Vulpes vulpes (Linnaeus, 1758)
Synonym: red fox

Order: Carnivora
Previous name(s): *Canis vulpes*
Gaelic: sionnach, madadh-ruadh

Conservation status None

Recognition and signs Since the extinction of the wolf, Britain's only extant native canid. Like a small fine-boned dog with reddish coat and black lower legs. Bushy tail ('brush') often with a white tip. On average, males are larger than females, but there is considerable overlap. Average length (including tail) 1-1.2m. Weight about 6kg for females and 7kg for males. Droppings very variable, 5-20cm long by about 2cm wide. Can be confused with those of dog, pine marten and wildcat (Davison *et al.*, 2002). The smell of urine scent-marks can be detected by some people. Frequency of droppings along linear features (e.g. fencelines) can be used to monitor population density (Webbon *et al.*, 2004). Fox footprints four-toed and dog-like, with claws visible, but with the two middle toes and claws parallel, rather than diverging (see Plate III). Tracks are often straighter and more purposeful than those of dogs. Foxes may sometimes be detected by their vocalisations, particularly a three-part bark and eerie screams during the mating season.

Ecology and behaviour Foxes are versatile and omnivorous predators/scavengers with a flexible breeding system. In each family territory only the dominant male and female breed. Subordinates may help with cub-rearing. If one or both are removed then the subordinates are likely to breed and increase the population. Foxes are able to exploit almost any habitat, and distribute themselves according to the resources available. Lockie (1964) found family territory sizes of up to 4,000ha in Wester Ross, whereas in urban habitats, (e.g. Edinburgh, Kolb 1986) they can be as small as 100ha. Scent marking is important in delimiting territory. Favoured food items in Highland include small rodents (particularly field voles), rabbits and hares, birds, carrion, invertebrates, frogs and fruit. Diet varies with season and locality. Secure dens, underground or among rocks, are used for breeding, but at other times of year, foxes may lie-up above ground. Mating takes place between December and February. After a gestation period of 53 days, 4-5 cubs are born in March/April, and weaned at 4 weeks old. Both parents bring food to the den. Cubs begin to disperse in August, but some may remain within the family range. Foxes may be active during the day or night depending on the level of disturbance. A fox may occasionally be met with on the hill in broad daylight and is probably as surprised by the encounter as you are.

History in Highland The history of the fox in the Highlands is a tale of survival against an onslaught of human antagonism. Unlike some of the other carnivores (wildcat, pine marten) this does not seem to have limited its range, either historically or in the present day.

Past and current management Foxes can legally be shot and snared to protect agricultural and game-rearing interests. Sheep at lambing time, free-range poultry and newly-released game-birds are particularly vulnerable. Controversy surrounds the extent to which foxes prey on live lambs as against taking those which are already dead. The fox, like any predator, will take the prey which is most efficient in energy terms. Domesticated stock or naïve game birds offer easy pickings, and the fox cannot be blamed for taking what is on offer. A study in Sutherland (Hewson, 1990) concluded that fox predation was a minor contributor to overall lamb losses, regardless of whether foxes were controlled or not. Mounted fox-hunting has never been a tradition in Highland, but a foot-pack of foxhounds continues to be operated by the Lochaber & Sunart Fox Destruction Society Ltd. Under the Protection of Wild Mammals Scotland Act 2002, the fox must be killed by shooting, after being flushed from cover by dogs.

Current distribution Probably ubiquitous in mainland Highland and Skye, but absent from all of the smaller islands (except possibly Carna in Loch Sunart – ITE Atlas and NBN give a 1971 record, but we have no recent confirmation). Berry (1983) also reports fox from Scalpay. Droppings, tracks in snow, and sightings of foxes are reported by hill walkers from ridges and summits at Munro level (over 3,000ft/1,000m).

Nature of records The majority of records (55%) are of signs (tracks and droppings) or road casualties (26%). Live sightings account for 17% and foxes shot or snared 2%. A further 260 records (excluded from these percentages) are historical ones from McGhie (2002).

Distributional trends Recorded from 133 Highland 10km squares in 1993 Atlas. The higher number of positive squares now (260) probably reflects more intensive recording effort rather than range expansion.

Where to look Populations of urban foxes have not (yet?) developed in Inverness to the extent that they have in cities such as Glasgow - but it may only be a matter of time. Foxes can be encouraged into gardens by the provision of food, but in an environment where familiarity with humans may be life-threatening, this could be unfair on the fox.

Fascinating fact The Ross-shire Journal reported on 26th May 1923 that a dozen live foxes were exported by rail from Bonar Bridge station to 'a sporting gentleman in the South Midlands of England' – presumably to be hunted.

Fox

Grey dot = 1999 and before   Black dot = 2000 and after

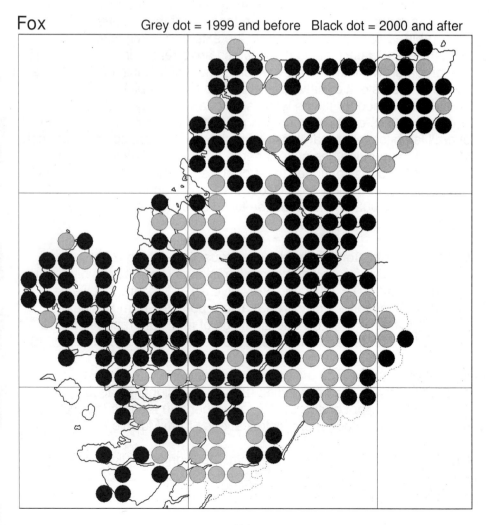

Badger

Order: Carnivora
Meles meles (Linnaeus, 1758)
Synonym: Eurasian badger
Previous name: *Ursus meles*
Gaelic: broc

Conservation status Protection of Badgers Act 1992 (as amended); W&C Act Schedule 6; SBL (social criterion)

Recognition and signs One of Britain's six indigenous Mustelids. A medium sized powerfully built omnivore with a distinctive white head and black stripes through the eyes. The dorsal and lateral body shows an overall grey colour from the white base and tip with a broad black band on the guard hairs. A less common but widespread colour variation is the erythristic or ginger coat, caused by two recessive genes. Occasionally, especially in the west, badgers are seen with white patches on the nose. An average head and body length of 75cm for males and 72cm for females but both with 15cm tails. Droppings vary from loose to firm and are similar in appearance to those of dog, but with a characteristic sweet musky smell. They are usually deposited in uncovered shallow pits. Where these are grouped together they are known as latrines and often signal a territorial boundary. Footprints show characteristic broad central pads with five forward facing toes and large front claws, which impress deeply in soft substrates (see Plate IV). Often the hind foot overprints the forefoot. Walking tracks show padding just either side of a median line.

Ecology and behaviour Badgers are opportunistic omnivores with a complex breeding cycle. The phenomenon of delayed implantation enables them to mate in any month, albeit usually in spring with a later rut in autumn, and yet produce their young in early spring the following year. Cubs are generally born in February or March and may remain within the group. Living in family groups known as clans they dig their setts, underground tunnels and chambers in suitably well drained substrata or utilise cavities in rock cairns. Setts can be found in dry moraines within wet moorland. Badgers prefer a mixture of woodland, short grazed turf and cropland. If sufficient foraging habitat is available they are able to survive the encroachment of urban sprawl (as around Inverness). Kruuk (1989) found territory sizes from 100 to 300ha in Speyside, and between 150 to 200ha in a West coast location. Earthworms are a nationally favoured food source and in Central Eastern Highland *Lumbricus terrestris* is taken in large quantities, whereas further west the much smaller *Lumbricus rubellus* generally means a lighter body weight for these badgers. In addition other invertebrates are important, together with rabbits and smaller mammals in certain areas. Sheep and deer carrion can be vital in hard winters especially in remote areas, whilst frogs and fruit add seasonal variation to the diet.

History in Highland Like other predatory and scavenging species, badgers have suffered persecution in the Highlands. Legal protection has reduced this and badger numbers have increased in certain areas. On Skye, no live setts have been recorded in recent decades, despite occasional badger sightings, but badgers were present within living memory (R. Balharry pers. comm.). A crofter in Upper Tote (NG55) reported having seen a badger 'making hay' (collecting bedding) during the 1950s. The widespread use of a cyanide-based agent for gassing rabbits in the 1960s, to facilitate forestry planting, may have caused the badgers' demise. Around 50 long-disused 'fossil' setts (represented by the pre-1999 dots on the map) have been identified, mostly in Sleat, and place-names such as Broc-bheinn (badger-hill) in Glen Drynoch (NG43), testify to their previous existence.

Past and current management Highland fox-hunting organisations have also expressed 'satisfaction' at kills of badgers! (Darling, 1947) Some estates killed badgers, whilst others protected them.

Current distribution In mainland Highland, badgers are found wherever ground conditions are suitable for establishing setts. They are currently absent from all the islands, but previously occurred in Skye (see history, above). The recent national survey by Scottish Badgers (Rainey *et al.*, 2009) found that 7% of the 1km squares surveyed in Highland contain main setts.

Nature of records Half of records (50%) are of setts or other signs (tracks, latrines, hair, 'snuffle holes' from feeding), 37% are road (and a few other) casualties, and 13% live sightings. A live badger may occasionally be met with on the hill in broad daylight, generally in quiet remote areas in west Highland; several such sightings are reported each year. In addition, 57 historical records from McGhie (2002) are not included in the above analysis.

Distributional trends Recorded from 120 Highland 10km squares in ITE Atlas, compared to 169 now. This probably reflects more intensive recording effort rather than any real range expansion.

Where to look The Strathspey badger hide offers badger-watches.

Fascinating fact Badgers were taken to the north of Sutherland in the early part of the 20th century and have done well among the regenerating birch woods (Darling, 1947).

Badger

Grey dot = 1999 and before   Black dot = 2000 and after

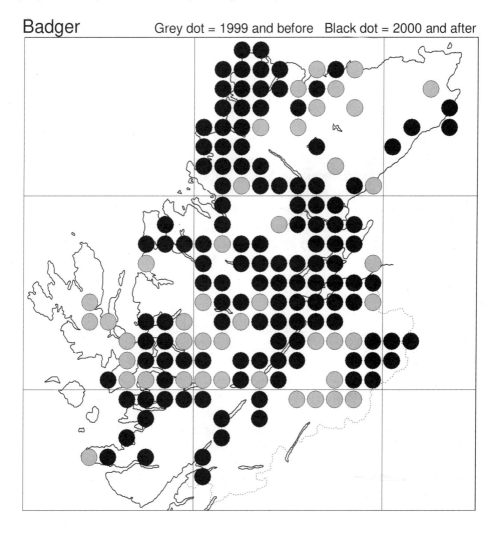

Otter

Order: Carnivora

Lutra lutra (Linnaeus, 1758)

Synonym: Eurasian otter

Gaelic: dòbhran, bèist-dhubh

Conservation status IUCN Red Data List 'Near Threatened'; EHD Annex II & IV (EPS); W&C Act Schedule 6; UK BAP; SBL (including social criterion)

Recognition and signs Otters are very distinctive and the only confusion could be between a mink and an otter cub. The fur is normally a dark chocolate brown, although animals with a lighter fur and albinos have been recorded. They have two layers of fur – an outer waterproof layer which protects the inner fur which has 50,000 hairs per cm^2. Individuals can be distinguished by markings on the lip and sometimes on the neck. They have short limbs, webbed feet and claws and on land they run with a typical "hump-back" gait. They swim very low in the water as the eyes, nose and ears are near the top of the head. It can be difficult to distinguish between an otter and a seal in the water. However, the otter is very buoyant due to the amount of air trapped in its fur, and frequently bursts out of the water as it surfaces. Also, when it dives you can usually spot the tail as it goes down. Otter signs are also very distinctive. The droppings (spraints) are deposited on conspicuous places, such as a large rock, tree stump, grassy hummocks, concrete ledges under bridges and where a river meets another river or loch. Spraint has an important communication role, and contains over 400 scent chemicals which pass on information to other otters. It is used to mark important places, such as holts, runs and freshwater pools, and to indicate the otter's breeding status to others. Spraint may also be deposited inter-tidally, offering shorter-term communications. Even to humans, spraint has a very characteristic smell and is slightly sweetish and fishy, as compared to mink scat which is very unpleasant! Spraint is usually black when fresh and becomes lighter with age. The prey remains (including fish bones, crab remains, feathers, etc.) contained in it can be used to give an indication of the diet. On occasion otters will also deposit anal jelly, which is a greyish, opaque secretion. The deposition of spraint in regular latrines acts like a fish fertiliser, and can result in the development of small areas of bright green nitrophilous grasses. (See Plates II and III for otter signs.) Like all mustelids, the otter has a five-toed footprint, unlike the dog or fox which shows four toes. The print of an adult is about 5-7cm across and if well preserved it is possible to see the clawmarks and webbing.

There may also be long marks left by the tail, particularly in snow. Otter runs, usually marked by spraint, can be found through areas of long grass and heather, where they form low tunnels through the vegetation.

Ecology and behaviour Otters use a variety of different habitats – freshwater lakes and ponds, rivers, estuaries and the coast. In coastal areas they are limited by the availability of freshwater pools – needed to wash the salt out of their fur and maintain thermo-insulation. In freshwater systems the home range of a female can be up to 30-40km; a male may overlap with 2 or more females, and have a home range of up to 70km. In coastal areas home ranges are much smaller - in parts of Skye as little as 3-4km. Otters may breed at any time of year. After a 61-day gestation, the female may have up to three cubs, which she then rears alone. Cubs do not leave the natal holt until they are about 8-10 weeks old, and may remain with their mother for up to 16 months or more before becoming independent.

In both salt and freshwater habitats the dominant prey is fish, although otters will also take amphibians, birds and small mammals, including rabbits. On the isle of Pabay rabbits form a large part of their diet. In freshwater areas they particularly like eels, but this is a major problem as the eel population has plummeted in recent years. On the coast they eat small eel-like inshore fish such as butterfish, blenny, sea scorpion and rockling. These four species, together with saithe, make up 85% of the diet of coastal otters.

History in Highland One of the earliest mentions of otters is found in Martin Martin's "A Description of The Western Islands Of Scotland *(circa 1695)* and he lists them with seals as "Amphibia"! In 1773 Johnson and Boswell travelled through Scotland to the islands off the West Coast and in his book Johnson commented on the fact that Scottish otters are bigger than those in England (Levi, 1984): *"Mr. Maclean, the heir of Col, a man of middle stature, informed me that he once shot an otter, of which the tail reached the ground, when he held up the head to a level with his own."* He also reported that *"white otters are sometimes seen."* The otter was hunted with hounds in Britain from the 13th century, and by the 16th century they were regarded as vermin with a bounty being paid for each one killed. Numbers declined drastically throughout most of Britain in the 1950s and 60s, largely because of the use of organochlorine chemicals in pesticides and herbicides which became concentrated in species at the top of the food chain, like otters.

However numbers in the Highlands remained more or less stable even though they were not legally protected in Scotland until 1982.

Past and current management Otters were historically trapped for their fur. Otter hunting has been illegal in Scotland since 1982 and they are now totally protected. It is also illegal to trap or move an otter without a licence and similarly a licence is required to visit holts. In the highlands the main threat to otters is from road kills. There is also a potential risk from muirburn and pollution, particularly oil spills.

Current distribution Otters are fairly widely distributed across Highland, especially along the west coast, and have been recorded from most of the islands.

Nature of records More than half of records (53%) are of signs, mostly spraints, but also tracks, paths and feeding remains. Live sightings comprise 30% and otters found dead 16% (mainly as road casualties, but also a few in creels or fyke nets). In addition, 271 historical records from McGhie (2002) are excluded from this analysis.

Distributional trends Recorded from 320 Highland 10km squares in the ITE Atlas, because this included records from the first comprehensive national otter survey (Green & Green 1980), which visited all but two of squares in mainland Highland and Skye. The fact that otters are recorded from fewer squares (285) in this Atlas probably reflects a lack of such comprehensive coverage since, rather than any diminution in the otter's range.

Where to look In freshwater systems otters tend to be nocturnal, but on the coast, particularly in the west, they are active on and off throughout the day and night. So this presents the best chance of seeing them. There are hides overlooking good otter habitat at Kylerhea on Skye (NG72) and at Garbh Eilean (Ardery) on Loch Sunart (NM76).

Fascinating fact Juvenile otters which have left their mothers too early can appear in very odd places. In Skye they have been known to go into the garage in Broadford, a playgroup in a village hall, through a catflap into a house, and various garages and outhouses! For advice in such circumstances or for orphaned and injured animals please contact the International Otter Survival Fund.

Otter

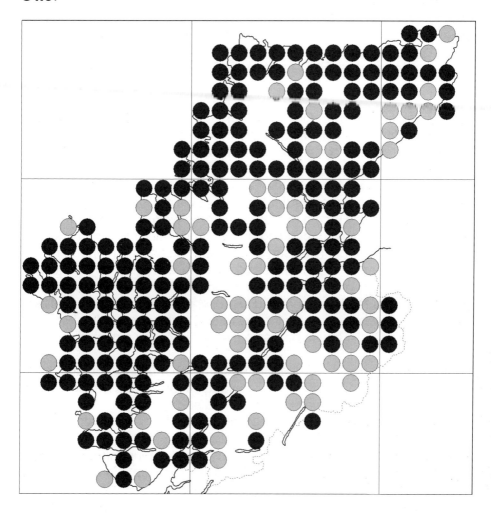

Grey dot = 1999 and before
Black dot = 2000 and after

Pine marten

Order: Carnivora

Martes martes (Linnaeus, 1758)   Previous name: *Mustela martes*
Synonym: marten cat, mart and sweetmart   Gaelic: taghan

Conservation status EHD Annex V; W&C Act Schedule 5; UKBAP; SBL

Recognition and signs One of Britain's six indigenous Mustelids. A small to medium agile climbing carnivore with a dark brown coat and distinctive throat and chest patch, which varies from pale cream in winter to a rich yellow or orange after spring moult. Large ears and longer legs distinguish it from the even rarer and smaller polecat. Mean length about 75cm for males (including tail), weight nearly 2kg; females 10% smaller in body length and 30% lighter in weight than males. Droppings are variable depending on diet, and difficult to distinguish from those of fox or cat (Davison *et al.*, 2002) unless fresh enough to retain their characteristic musky smell. They are roughly 4-12cm long and up to 1.9cm in diameter. They can be black, twisted and dry when containing fur or feathers; pale and loose when carrion is taken; yellow after raiding bumblebee nests for larvae and pollen; or purple after eating blaeberries. Rowan berries pass through semi-digested.

Ecology and behaviour Pine martens are opportunistic and adaptable omnivores. As noted above, a wide variety of food types is taken; birds, invertebrates, carrion, small mammals and seasonal fruits. Wild food is augmented in some places by food intended for birds in private gardens, and by people feeding them deliberately.
The phenomenon of delayed implantation enables pine martens to mate from June to August and yet produce their young from mid March to mid/late April in the following year. The young (average three kits) leave the natal den between mid June to mid July and disperse from mid August to the end October.
Two Highland studies (Balharry, 1993; Halliwell, 1997) both found that although pine marten home ranges were of very variable size, they contained an approximately equal area of woodland per marten (about 125ha) – the remainder being made up of open country.
Deforestation, and the replacement of native hardwoods by regimented conifers, has deprived martens of secure natal den sites (tree-holes), as well as reducing the availability of prey. They are forced to use less than ideal ground-level sites - typically root plates of windblown trees,

piles of brash or logs, rock crevices or burrows. In turn this has made them vulnerable to predation by foxes. Both inhabited and disused buildings are also now used, which can occasionally be problematic for people (Brown & Birks, 2006). Old large bird nests, and owl or duck nest boxes are occasionally used and offer more security.

History in Highland Pine martens are native to Scotland and presumably followed the spread of their woodland habitat northwards at the end of the ice age.

Past and current management A combination of large scale deforestation and intensive persecution from the mid 19th century, with the formation of sporting estates, together with the introduction of breech-loading firearms and steel traps, brought the pine marten to near extinction by the turn of the 20th century. They only survived in the extreme the North West Highlands (Langley & Yalden, 1977). With legal protection, conservation management is now a priority. Methods have been devised to protect vulnerable poultry and game birds (Balharry, 1998) rather than killing martens. Also, a sliding hen-house door controlled by a photoelectric cell can reduce or even eliminate predation, once the hens understand that at dusk the door closes.

Current distribution Now found in most areas of mainland Highland having spread south-eastwards from their stronghold in the north-west. Absent from all Highland islands except Skye, which they have only colonised since the opening of the Skye Bridge in October 1995.

Nature of records The most frequent category of records (42%) is of signs, with sightings next (32%) and road casualties third (16%). In addition, 70 historical records from McGhie (2002) are excluded from the above analysis.

Distributional trends Recorded from 184 Highland 10km squares in 1993 Atlas compared to 169 now. This probably represents a fairly stable situation, suggesting that the pine marten has consolidated its range within mainland Highland (whilst continuing to expand to the south-east (Balharry *et al.*, 1996)).

Where to look Many B&Bs advertise that they feed pine martens. They are also seen occasionally from the Strathspey badger hide.

Fascinating fact To offset the loss of tree-holes, the Vincent Wildlife Trust has designed marten breeding boxes (Birks JDS *et al.,* 2006). From 2003 these have been increasingly successful in two Forestry Commission conifer woodlands. In 2007 the first site produced 85% occupancy and 20% breeding; with 100% occupancy and 40% breeding at the second site. These boxes can also be used as mitigation when the martens' use of houses as natal den sites creates problems.

Pine marten

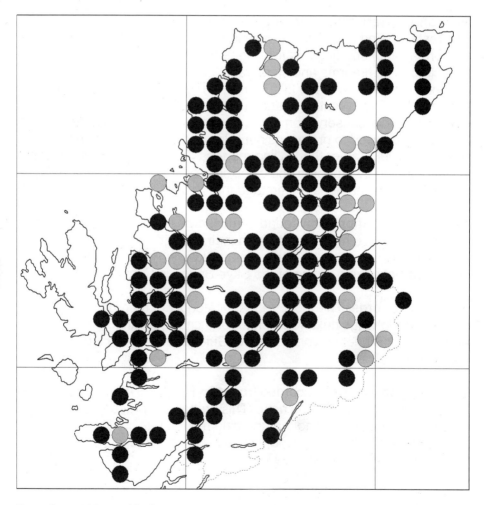

Grey dot = 1999 and before
Black dot = 2000 and after

Stoat

Mustela erminea Linnaeus, 1758

Order: Carnivora

Gaelic: neas, nios

Conservation status Bern Convention Appendix III

Recognition and signs The only certain way to distinguish between a stoat and a weasel, at a glance, is the black tail-tip of the stoat. This is present whether the stoat is in its brown summer pelage or its white winter ermine. Although stoats are, on average, larger than weasels, there is an overlap between small female stoats and large male weasels. Male stoats measure about 330-430mm in total length, and females 320-380mm. The tail is about 40% of the combined head and body length. Adult stoats weigh between 200 and 400g. The stoat's underside is cream whereas that of the weasel is white, and the join between the brown upper and pale under surface is wavy in the weasel but straight in the stoat (- a handy alliterative way to remember!) Skulls found in raptor or owl pellets can only be separated by species at either end of the range of variation (i.e. a male stoat or a female weasel) because the dentition is identical. Similarly, the droppings, tracks and feeding signs (such as the puncture marks left by the canine teeth) of stoat and weasel overlap in size, and can only be reliably distinguished at either end of the size range. For example, stoat droppings can be 40-80mm long and weasel droppings 30-60mm long. So a dropping 70mm long is likely to be stoat, and one of 35mm weasel. But a dropping 40-60mm long could be from either.

Ecology and behaviour Stoats use a wide variety of habitats, from lowland agricultural landscapes to the higher moorlands. They like to remain under cover, and frequently follow linear features such as stone dykes or hedgerows. The stoat's preferred food is rabbits (often larger than the stoat itself) which make up on average over half of their diet. Smaller prey, such as mice, voles, birds and their eggs are taken, particularly by the smaller females, which can pass through vole tunnels. Stoats will climb trees to find prey and will also raid nest boxes. Home range sizes are very variable, depending on food availability. Individuals do not overlap with others of the same sex, but each male will overlap with several females. Males may temporarily wander farther afield in search of mates during the breeding season. Stoats are mainly nocturnal in winter and diurnal in summer.

The stoat has an extraordinary breeding cycle, relying on delayed implantation. Females make their breeding dens in hollow logs, stone dykes, rabbit burrows, drains or anywhere else which offers appropriate shelter. She gives birth to a litter of 6-9 young in April or May. Before the young are weaned, a passing male will mate with both mother and any daughters. Because of the short lifespan and quick turnover in the stoat population, he is unlikely to be their own father, and thus inbreeding does not seem to be a problem. The young, including already-mated females, disperse at about 3 months old, in July/August. The fertilised embryo does not implant into the womb lining, but stays in a state of suspended animation for 9-10 months. Implantation is initiated by increasing day-length the following Spring, and a 'normal' pregnancy of 4 weeks then takes place, before the cycle begins again. Because of their great reproductive capacity, stoat populations can respond quickly to changes in prey availability. Their populations tend to fluctuate, along with the rabbit population, in response to outbreaks of myxomatosis. Stoats are preyed upon by foxes, cats (wild and feral) and the larger raptors such as buzzards and eagles.

History in Highland A native predator, probably rarer in the days before rabbit populations were so widespread. Stoats are thought to have survived the last glaciation in the tundra landscape of southern Britain, and re-colonised Scotland from there. The faunas describe them as widespread and particularly 'plentiful' in areas where rabbits were increasing.

Past and current management Has been regarded as 'vermin' for centuries and subjected to persecution, particularly by sporting estates during Victorian times, for its supposed impact on ground-nesting game birds. This is thought to be more serious where wild, rather than reared, birds are the quarry species. Stoats can still legally be trapped and stoat traps mounted in tunnels may be encountered in Highland today.

Current distribution Stoats are present throughout the mainland and on Skye and Raasay. Harvie-Brown & Macpherson (1904) reported one being shot on Handa in 1902, but assumed it to have been taken to the island by a bird of prey. Another was seen swimming from Skye to the mainland.

Nature of records Most records are of sightings (78%), as the stoat is an inquisitive animal and not greatly intimidated by people. Animals found dead (including roadkill) make up 17% of records, and signs 5%.

Distributional trends Recorded from 66 10km squares in ITE atlas, compared to 154 here. This probably reflects an increase in recording effort rather than any significant expansion of range.

Where to look An encounter with stoats is usually a fortuitous happening, unless the site of a breeding den is known. In which case, the antics of the female and young as they practice for their predatory existence by pouncing on each other can be a joy to watch. Families of up to 9 kits with their mother have been observed, and words such as 'playing' 'dancing' and 'hightailing' give an impression of the stoat's attitude to life. Highland observers have reported seeing stoats carrying voles, killing rabbits, chasing a lapwing on the shore (unsuccessfully), retrieving a bird carcass from the road and stealing a cooked duck wing! Otherwise it is very difficult to set out deliberately to see them – although roadside stone dykes offer a good prospect. Once you know it is there, a stoat can be 'squeaked up' by sucking the back of your hand to imitate the squeal of a distressed rabbit.

Fascinating fact Harvie-Brown (1892) reported that stoats had been recorded at the observatory on the summit of Ben Nevis 'from 1884 onwards' – thus qualifying (along with humans) as Britain's highest mammal.

Stoat

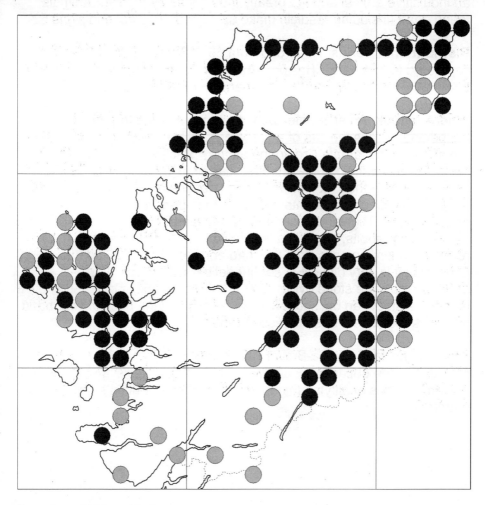

Grey dot = 1999 and before
Black dot = 2000 and after

Weasel

Order: Carnivora

Mustela nivalis Linnaeus, 1766 Gaelic: neas-bheag, nios-bheag

Conservation status Bern convention Appendix III

Recognition and signs A long, low, lithe animal similar in shape to the stoat but smaller in size. Males 230-310mm long; females 210-240mm long. Average weight males 125g females 70g. The weasel lacks the black tail-tip of the stoat and the tail length is shorter (20-30%) relative to the combined head and body length. The underside is white rather than cream, and its edge is wavy rather than straight. (Remember: wavy weasel; straight stoat.) Unlike the stoat, the weasel does not usually moult into a white coat in winter in Britain (although one or two instances have been recorded). Males are approximately 1/3rd larger than females and overlap in size with female stoats.

Weasel and stoat skulls are very similar and their dentition is identical. So when found in raptor or owl pellets, only skulls at either end of the size range (i.e. a male stoat or a female weasel) can be assigned to species. Similarly, the droppings, tracks and feeding signs (such as the puncture marks left by the canine teeth) of the two species overlap in size, and can only be reliably distinguished at either end of the range. Weasel droppings are 30-60mm long, and stoat droppings can be 40-80mm long. So a dropping of 70mm long is likely to be stoat, and 35mm weasel. But a dropping 40-60mm long could be from either.

Ecology and behaviour Weasels live in a variety of habitats wherever their main prey, small rodents, are found. They are common in agricultural areas, grasslands, and young conifer plantations, but less common than stoats in upland areas. Weasels are adapted to prey on small rodents, such as mice and voles, and can hunt within their tunnels. They will also takes juvenile rabbits, birds and eggs. The larger males take more rabbits than the smaller females. Birds, including small passerines (e.g. blue tits) in nest boxes, are particularly targeted when rodents are scarce. Weasel predation can have a significant impact on small rodent populations. Being long and thin, weasels have high energy requirements and need to eat about 1/3rd of their body weight per day. The female weasel makes her breeding den in any small secure hole - rodent or rabbit burrows, mole tunnels, stone walls, tree holes etc. Unlike the stoat, the weasel does not have delayed implantation, and undergoes a more 'normal' breeding cycle.

Gestation lasts about 35 days and a litter of 4-8 young is born in spring or summer. In peak vole years, two litters may occur. Young are weaned after 4 weeks and begin to disperse at 12 weeks old.
Home range size varies with food availability. Males have a larger home range and will overlap with several females, but individuals do not overlap with others of the same sex. Weasels tend to be diurnal in their activity.

History in Highland Unlike the stoat, there are no records of weasels having survived the last glaciation in southern England. But they were probably one of the earliest colonists after the ice retreated, following their small rodent prey.

Current distribution Probably widely distributed throughout the mainland due to the ubiquity of its prey. Recorded only from Skye among the islands.

Nature of records The majority of records (74%) are of live sightings, with 14% road casualties, 5% predator kills (mainly cat), 5% from signs and 3% trapped.

Distributional trends Recorded from 65 10km squares in ITE atlas, compared to 139 now. This probably represents increased recording effort rather than range expansion.

Past and current management The weasel is still legally trapped by gamekeepers although its impact on ground-nesting game birds is likely to be less than that of the stoat.

Where to look It is extremely difficult to predict where weasels may be seen – you just have to be lucky! Like the stoat, once you know a weasel is there it can be attracted closer by 'squeaking up' - sucking the back of your hand to make a high-pitched squeal.

Fascinating fact Because of the size difference between male and female weasels, females were at one time thought to be a separate species, called the cane-weasel.

Weasel

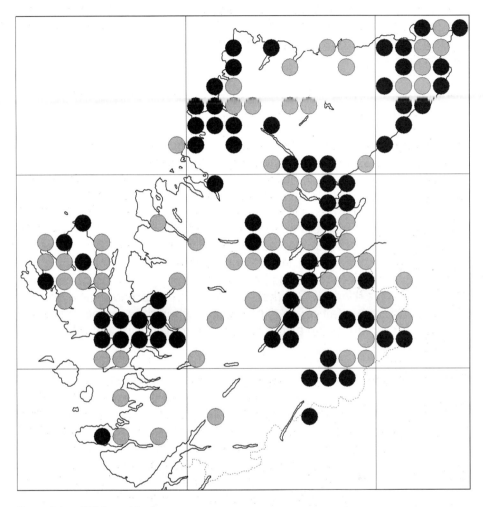

Grey dot = 1999 and before
Black dot = 2000 and after

Polecat and feral ferret

Mustela putorius Linnaeus, 1758 (Polecat)
Mustela furo Linnaeus, 1758 (Ferret)
Mustela furo x putorius (Polecat-ferret)
Synonym: foulmart

Order: Carnivora
Gaelic: feòcallan
Gaelic: fearaid

Conservation status Polecat: W&C Act Schedule 5; UKBAP
Feral ferret/polecat-ferret: none

Recognition and signs The ferret is the domesticated form of the polecat. Whilst white or sandy ferrets are unlikely to be confused with polecats, polecat-ferrets (which are not necessarily crosses between a ferret and a true polecat, but just dark-coloured ferrets) look very similar. In general the coat of the true polecat is darker all over and the black mask on the face comes down to meet the rhinarium (nose-pad). Pale or sandy ferrets can also be confused with pale colour forms of the mink. For this atlas, all animals have been assumed to be ferrets unless positively determined as polecats from a photograph or carcass by the national expert (JDS Birks). Both creatures are long, low and short-legged, with a tail which can bush out when they are alarmed. When frightened they can also emit a smelly musk from a gland beneath the tail.

Ecology and behaviour The polecat's name arises from the French poule-chat, meaning a cat which feeds on chickens. Domestic ferrets are used for bolting rabbits from their burrow so that they can be caught in a net or shot, and the rabbit is the preferred prey of both the polecat and feral ferret. However, in the wild, both animals will also feed on ground-nesting birds, small rodents, frogs, lizards and whatever else they can catch. Nothing is known of the home range sizes and breeding habits of feral ferrets or polecats in Highland.

History in Highland Polecats were formerly widespread throughout Britain, but were persecuted to extinction in Scotland by the early 20th Century because of their predation on domestic fowl and game birds (Langley & Yalden, 1977). They had been thought long extinct in Highland, but a recent survey (Birks, 2008) has revealed animals which have been confirmed as polecats. Statistical analysis (Solow *et al.*,2006) indicates that these are more likely to result from a recent introduction, rather than being remnants of the original native polecat population. Nothing is known of the history of ferret-keeping in Highland. Presumably they were not widespread until rabbits became more prevalent during the 19th century.

Past and current management Whilst true polecats are now fully protected, feral ferrets are not. This means that polecats, along with ferrets, may be vulnerable to predator control by gamekeepers, unless awareness of their existence is raised within the area where they occur.

Current distribution Populations of feral ferrets appear to be established around Dingwall, in Strathspey and possibly east Sutherland and Caithness. Other records may result from occasional ferrets left behind after going to ground whilst being used for rabbiting.

Feral ferret Grey dot = 1999 and before   Black dot = 2000 and after

Berry (1983) reports them from Canna, but we have no records. The only confirmed records of true polecats are from the east of Caithness and Sutherland, where it seems that they have been introduced.

Distributional trends The feral ferret was recorded from 17 Highland 10km squares in the ITE atlas, compared to 38 now. There were no records of polecat from Highland in the ITE atlas. It has so far been found in 4 10km squares and may yet expand farther.

Nature of records Three-quarters of records are of road casualties, with the remainder mostly live sightings and a very few trapped or snared.

Polecat   Grey dot = 1999 and before   Black dot = 2000 and after

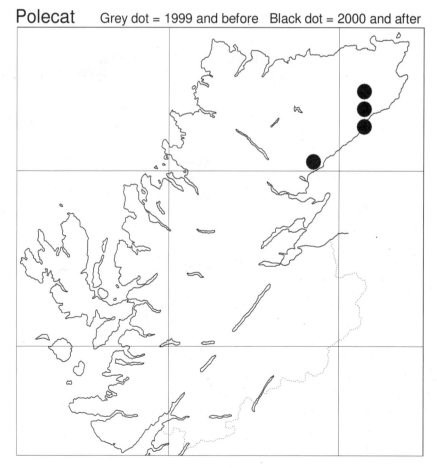

American mink

Order: Carnivora

Mustela vison Schreber, 1777

Alternative name: *Neovison vison*

Synonym: mink

Gaelic: mionc

Conservation status W&C Act Schedule 9

Recognition and signs A small mustelid similar in size and shape to the ferret, and much smaller than the otter (see Plate II). Average weights of males about 1kg, females 500-700g. Mink can come in a variety of colour forms, from dark glossy brown to nearly white, and usually have a white patch on the chin. Pale coloured mink can be confused with feral ferrets. Their droppings can look very similar to those of otter but are distinguished from them by their foul, rather than sweet, smell. Tracks sometimes show only 4 of the 5 toes, in a characteristic splayed-out star shape.

Ecology and behaviour The mink is an adaptable largely aquatic predator which can live in fresh water or the sea. They can feed on fish, aquatic and terrestrial invertebrates, amphibians, birds, eggs, rabbits and small mammals. They will also eat carrion washed up on the shore and occasionally prey on domestic poultry and game birds. Mink tend to occupy linear home ranges of 1-6km, along watercourses or the coast. Males overlap with several females, but each sex does not overlap with others of the same gender. Males may leave their territory in spring to seek mates more widely. They play no part in rearing the young. Each mink will have several dens within its range, made in rocks, tree roots or rabbit burrows close to the water's edge. Females have one litter per year of up to 6 young, usually born in May. Gestation varies in length because of delayed implantation, but young are born 28 days after the embryo implants. Young are suckled for 6-8 weeks and are fully grown at about 4 months. Juveniles can disperse long distances in autumn. Whilst not as well adapted as otters to the aquatic environment (being more buoyant and lacking the flattened tail) they can swim several km in the open sea and therefore pose a threat to seabirds nesting on otherwise predator-free islands. Mink are less well able to dive than otters, diving less deeply and remaining submerged for shorter durations. These limited aquatic abilities make them more likely to be found in the slow-flowing shallow water courses also favoured by water voles.

History in Highland Native to North America, mink were initially introduced, from the 1940's onwards, as a captive animal in fur farms at various places in Highland (Cuthbert, 1973). They soon escaped and began to form free-living feral populations. On the mainland, the Black Isle was the only location north of the Great Glen to be colonised by 1972. Since then, mink seem to have spread more quickly up the west coast than in the east. Initially it was feared that they might pose a threat to the otter population through competition for food, but their predatory impact on water vole and seabird colonies is now thought to be a more serious problem.

Past and current management Since their establishment in the wild, control of mink has been sporadic and uneven, usually in response to specific predation incidents. A project targeting mink trapping at seabird breeding islands off the west coast has been successful in limiting their impact (Craik,1997), but constant vigilance is required. After two initial mink monitoring and control projects, in the Cairngorms and North-west Highland, a new project began in 2011 aiming at strategic mink control across the whole of northern Highland (Harrington *et al.* 2008). The Scottish Mink Initiative employs a project officer who runs a network of volunteers to monitor mink rafts designed by the Game Conservation & Wildlife Trust. These detect the presence of mink by registering footprints on a wet clay pad. When mink are detected, traps are deployed to catch them for humane killing.

Current distribution Mink are now widely distributed across the western part of Highland, and are gradually progressing northwards up both the west and the east coasts. They are also found on some of the larger inland river systems such as the Conon.

Nature of records Half of all records are of live sightings, with the remainder divided approximately equally between: road casualties; mink shot and/or trapped; and identifications from signs.

Distributional trends Recorded from 33 10km squares in ITE atlas 1993, compared to 90+ now. This reflects genuine range expansion.

Where to look Mink are quite bold and will often stop to take a good look at you if encountered by the waterside. Easiest to see on the west coast, in sea lochs and around islands.

Fascinating fact Research in the Western Isles (Clode & Macdonald, 1995) has shown that where otters and mink occur together, they each specialise more closely on particular food types, with mink tending to favour terrestrial prey and crustaceans whereas otters concentrate on fish. Mink undertake what is known as 'surplus killing'. This is not the result of malevolence on their part, but an instinctive reaction to an abundance of prey behaving in an agitated manner, as at a seabird breeding colony, or in a henhouse.

American mink

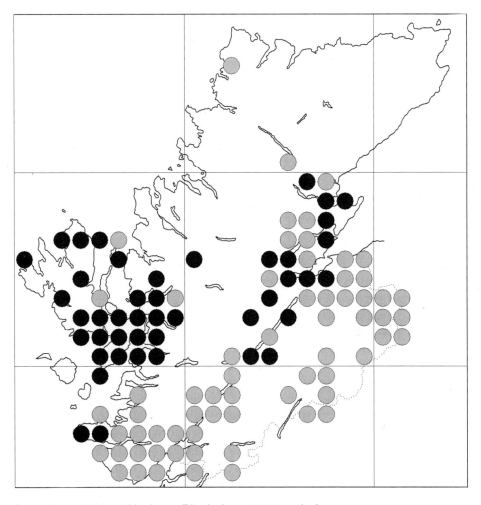

Grey dot = 1999 and before   Black dot = 2000 and after

Common seal

Phoca vitulina Linnaeus, 1758
Synonym: harbour seal

Order: Pinnipedia
Gaelic : ròn cumanta

Conservation status EHD Annex II; Bern Convention Appendix III;
MSA 2010

Recognition and signs The smaller of the two British seal species.
Although grey seals are on average larger, and males of both species
are larger than females, there is a considerable overlap in size
(particularly between male common seals and female grey seals) and
neither size nor colour are reliable distinguishing features. The
appearance of a seal's coat can differ markedly between wet and dry
states. The common seal has a more dished face, with dog-shaped
profile and nostrils which meet to form a 'Y' shape. Common seals
often assume a characteristic 'banana' posture when hauled out.
Although seals do leave tracks and droppings on sandbanks, you are
more likely to see the seals themselves!

Ecology and behaviour The common seal generally lives closer
inshore than the grey seal, but may still travel long distances to feed.
Common seals haul out on sandbanks and rocky islets, particularly
those which remain isolated by water at low tide, usually in the more
sheltered firths, sea lochs and estuaries. Sometimes, both common
and grey seals will haul out together.
Birth of pups takes place in summer (June/July) on the haul-out sites,
each female having only a single pup. She will mate again before it is
weaned. Mating takes place in the water and it is thought that males
use sound to display to females (Van Parijs *et al.*, 2003). Delayed
implantation of the embryo means that true pregnancy does not begin
until up to 3 months later. Unlike grey seal pups, common seal pups
are born with their adult fur, having lost the white coat in the womb, and
are able to swim immediately. They are suckled for 3-4 weeks, but then
have to learn to fish for themselves. Common seals feed on a variety of
different fish species, depending on what is most easily available: –
sand-eels, cod, herring, flatfish, or octopus (Thompson *et al.*, 1996).
They will travel up to 75km between haul-out sites and up to 60km from
their haul-outs to forage. They sometimes swim up rivers and have
been seen in the centre of Inverness and even in Loch Ness

(Williamson, 1988). Common seals moult annually in August and spend more time on land during this period.

History in Highland Probably present ever since the seas around Scotland thawed after the last ice age. They were hunted during the Mesolithic, and probably at all times since. Pennant (1777) reported that "In some places the skins and oil are an article of commerce."

Past and current management Common seals were formerly hunted for their skins and fat, and because of their propensity to feed on salmon at river mouths – within sight of humans. More recently they are regarded as a pest at marine fish farms, but caged fish can be protected by anti-predator nets and sonic seal-scarers. Now that they are protected throughout the year, a licence is needed before they can be shot because of damage to fisheries. The extent to which seals impact upon human use of the fish resource (or *vice versa*?) continues to be hotly debated.

Current distribution Widely distributed around the coast of Highland, with significant congregations in the east coast firths (up to 380 seen in the Dornoch Firth) and west coast sea lochs.

Nature of records The vast majority of records (95%) are of live sightings, with the remaining 5% being seals found dead on the beach.

Distributional trends Recorded from 75 Highland 10km squares in the ITE Atlas, compared to 85 now. No trend apparent.

Where to look There are many common seal haul-outs close enough inshore to be watched from the roadside (although please find a safe lay-by first). Seal-watching boat trips are offered at many coastal towns and villages. The Dolphin and Seal Centre accessed from the northbound carriageway of the A9 north of the Kessock Bridge is open during the summer season, and has hydrophones which allow the underwater sounds made by seals to be heard.

Common seal

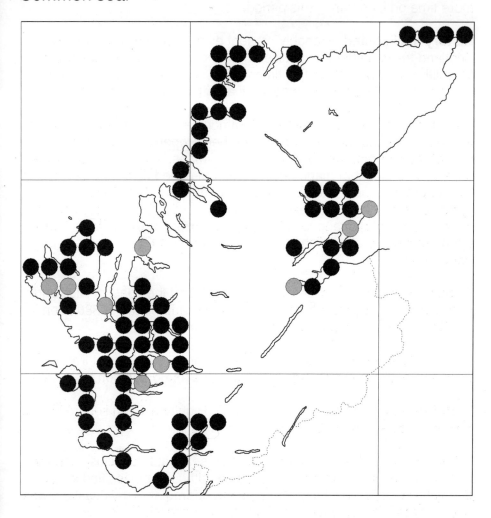

Grey dot = 1999 and before
Black dot = 2000 and after

Grey seal
Halichoerus grypus (Linnaeus, 1758)
Synonym: Atlantic seal

Order: Pinnipedia
Gaelic: ròn mòr

Conservation status EHD Annex II; Bern Convention Appendix III; MSA 2010

Recognition and signs On average, larger than the common seal, and males larger than females. Because there is a considerable overlap (particularly between male common seals and female grey seals) size is not a reliable indicator of species, except in the case of mature bull grey seals which may weigh more than 300kg. The coat colours and patterns of the two species are quite variable and cannot be used to differentiate them. The grey seal has a straight profile or Roman nose (particularly the males) in contrast to the common seal's dog-like profile, and nostrils which converge thus \ /, but do not meet at the bottom to form a 'Y'. Grey seals on the haul-out are more vocal than common seals, and can often be heard 'singing'.

Ecology and behaviour The grey seal is the seal of the open ocean, travelling and breeding further offshore than the common seal. Grey seals tend to haul out on more distant rocky islands. They will travel more than 350km between haul-outs and up to 145km from haul-outs to foraging sites (Thompson *et al.*, 1996), travelling as far as the edge of the continental shelf. Their diet is similar to that of the common seal, consisting of a variety of fish; sand eels, members of the cod family, herring, flatfish and other species. Grey seals are thus less likely to be seen in sheltered waters close inshore – but outwith the breeding season may sometimes haul out with common seals. Pupping takes place in November, on remote rocky skerries or in sea caves. Each female has only a single pup. Pups are born with a white juvenile coat and are unable to swim. Once they have moulted into their adult coats at 2-3 weeks old they can take to the water. Females mate about 2 weeks after giving birth. Males compete for mates and a dominant bull may father many pups. Implantation of the embryo is delayed by up to 10 weeks, followed by an 8-9 month pregnancy, so that the next pup is born a year later.

History in Highland Probably present ever since the seas around Scotland thawed after the last ice age. They were hunted during the

Mesolithic, and probably at all times since. Harvie-Brown (1895) reported that they were "not uncommon around Brora where Mr Houstoun shot a fine one in 1893".

Past and current management Grey seals were formerly hunted as a resource for their skins and fat. The population reached a low level at the beginning of the 20th century, but has recovered since, to the extent that they area now regarded as a problem in some quarters (Lambert, 2002). Scotland holds most of the UK population. They are still regarded as a competitor with humans for fish and consequently persecuted (illegally). They are also regarded as a pest at salmon netting stations and fish farms, but caged fish can be protected with anti-predator nets and sonic seal-scarers. Now that they are protected throughout the year, a licence is needed before they can be shot because of damage to fisheries.

Current distribution Grey seals are widespread all around the Highland coastline, except for the sheltered innermost parts of the east coast firths and heads of west coast sea-lochs. They may be seen in large numbers on some haul-outs (e.g. 100+ on the north end of Stroma).

Nature of records The vast majority of records (93%) are of sightings, with the remaining 7% being seals found dead on the beach, half of which were pups.

Distributional trends Recorded from 85 10km squares in the ITE atlas compared to 72 now. However, the ITE Atlas included records from the Sea Mammal Research Unit, who are better able to visit the more remote sites than are HBRG members!

Where to look Can be seen hauled out on remoter rocky coasts. Some of the seal-watching boat trips offered at many coastal towns and villages may visit these. Alternatively, some offshore ferry routes, such as Gill's Bay (ND37) to Orkney, pass fairly close to grey seal haul-outs.

Fascinating fact Annual grey seal pup-production is monitored by the Sea Mammal Research Unit at St. Andrews. Breeding haul-outs are photographed from the air with thermal imaging cameras. The body heat of the seals makes them show up as white blobs which are then counted back in the lab.

Grey seal

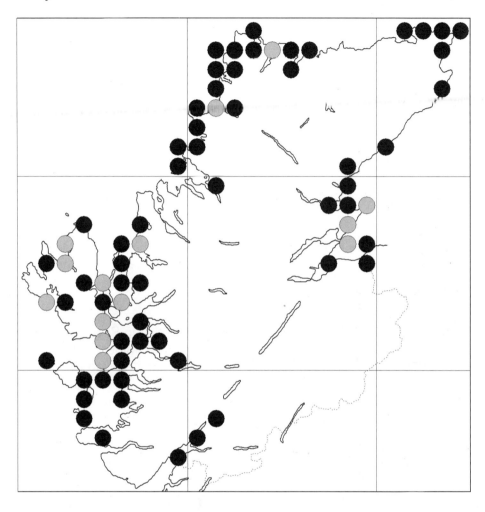

Grey dot = 1999 and before
Black dot = 2000 and after

Wild boar

Sus scrofa Linnaeus, 1758

Synonym: wild pig

Order: Artiodactyla

Gaelic: torc, muc fhiadhain

Conservation status None

Recognition and signs A large, dark-coloured, hairy pig. Males are bigger and heavier than females and have tusks. Piglets are paler brown with horizontal cream stripes. Footprints show the two main toes (hoofs) and often also the two side toes on each foot, because these are larger than those of the other ungulates. Signs of feeding are distinctive, with furrows and patches of earth and vegetation turned over by the snout. Dung pellets are larger than those of deer and of irregular size and shape.

Ecology and behaviour Wild boar are largely herbivorous, but will also eat carrion and small birds, mammals, eggs and chicks found on the ground. They tend to remain in cover during the day, emerging to feed at night.

History in Highland Wild boar were formerly native to Scotland but are thought to have become extinct by the 13th century (Yalden, 1999). Boar bones dating from 800-100BC have been found at High Pasture Cave (NG51) in Skye (S. Birch, pers. comm.). Recently the use of wild boar in preparing ground for woodland regeneration schemes seems to have resulted in escapes. We have no evidence yet that a breeding population is established, but this may only be a matter of time. The genetic constitution of animals originating from captivity is not known - they may be crosses with domestic pigs rather than pure wild boar.

Past and current management As a large and tasty animal which can be quite damaging to agriculture it is perhaps not surprising that the original native population of wild boar was hunted to extinction. The fate of the current escapees remains to be seen.

Current distribution All wild boar records so far are from the area between Loch Arkaig and Glen Garry in Lochaber.

Nature of records All records are of foraging signs.

114

Wild boar

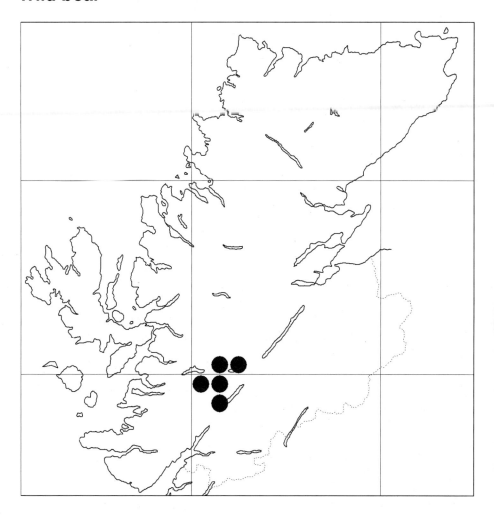

Grey dot = 1999 and before
Black dot = 2000 and after

Red deer

Cervus elaphus Linnaeus 1758
Gaelic: fiadh (deer); damh, damh ruadh (stag); eilid, agh-fèidh (hind);
mang, ruadhag, laogh (calf)

Conservation status Deer Scotland Act 1996 Close seasons
(Scotland): stags 21st October - 30th June; hinds 16th February - 20th
October; SBL (social criterion)

Recognition and signs Although red deer are the largest deer species
in Britain, highland red deer living on the open hill are smaller and
lighter in weight than those living in woodland or in deer parks. In
upland habitats stags (males) measure about 1.2m tall at the shoulder
and hinds (females) about 1.1m. Although weights can vary throughout
the year, stags average around 114kg and hinds around 75kg. Red
deer get their name from their bright red-brown summer coats, but are a
duller brown in winter. Colour variations are unusual although white
animals are occasionally reported. Adults do not have pale spots. The
pale beige or cream rump patch is diagnostic, extending dorsally above
the short tail, and not outlined in black as it is in sika or fallow deer.
Red deer are closely related to sika and able to hybridise with them.
Such hybrids will sometimes show a much darker coat. Red deer
young (calves) are spotted, as are those of fallow, sika and roe deer.
Antlers, which are only borne by the stags, are shed annually (in spring)
and re-grown in time for the mating season or 'rut' in autumn. Although
older stags tend to have more complex antlers, the number of points
does not correspond directly with the stag's age. Cast antlers may
occasionally be found, particularly where deer jump fences, or at
wallows. They should be left on the hill because the deer chew them to
reclaim the calcium.
Red deer tracks (see Plate IV) show the two slots or cleaves of each
foot and, apart from the larger tracks of adult stags, overlap in size and
shape with those of other deer. When fresh the droppings are black
and shiny but they soon become dull. They are cylindrical in shape, 20-
25 mm long by 13-18mm across (for adult deer), and often have a point
at one end, with the other end being either rounded or slightly concave.

Ecology and behaviour Red deer society is a matriarchy and, for
most of the year, red deer live in two separate groups. The hinds,
calves and immature stags tend to occupy the better quality grazings,

leaving the mature stags to cope with coarser vegetation. Hind groups are 'hefted' to their home area whereas stags tend to wander more. Large groups of hinds may sometimes be seen scattered over the hillsides, gathering together if disturbed. Both sexes move seasonally in response to weather and food availability, tending to occupy the high tops and corries in summer and lower ground in winter. Red deer in woodlands or forestry plantations live in smaller groups, sometimes resting and ruminating by day, and emerging at night to feed.

The sexes only come together for the autumn 'rut' in October. During this time stags vie with each other to hold a harem of hinds. Although stags will lock antlers in challenges, body weight is more critical in determining the outcome. Stags without antlers, called 'hummels' often attract and hold harems. The quality of the stag's roar signals his fitness to the hinds. Dominant stags do not eat during the rut and eventually become exhausted, allowing subordinates to gain access to the hinds. After the rut the sexes go their separate ways. Calves are born the following May/June, usually in secluded spots on high ground. Hinds leave their very young calves hidden in vegetation for long periods whilst they graze. Such calves have not been abandoned and should be left well alone. Calves are weaned after 8 months and continue to follow their mothers until the next calf is born. Red deer have been the subject of very long term studies by Cambridge University and others on the island of Rum (see Clutton-Brock *et al.*, 1982). For hybridisation with sika see that species.

History in Highland Red deer are native, having colonised Britain following the development of their original woodland habitat after the ice age. Bones dating from 800-100BC have been found at High Pasture Cave (NG51) in Skye (S. Birch, pers. comm.). Red deer antler was a valuable commodity for tool-making during the Mesolithic and Neolithic, until the development of metal tools in the Bronze Age (Mulville, 2010), and red deer would have continued to be hunted for their meat and skins thereafter. More recently, numbers fell to low levels in the 18th century because of exploitation for food during the time of peak human population, prior to the highland clearances.

Past and current management Since management for sport became prevalent in the 19th century, there have been numerous introductions of red deer to many areas, including some islands. Some landowners tried to improve their stock by bringing in larger and heavier park deer such as those from the Warnham Deer Park in England. Traditional

117

management involved selective culling of older stags and those in poor condition. Similarly, yeld hinds (hinds with no calves) and hinds in poor condition were culled. The number of stags culled per year contributes to calculating the capital value of Highland sporting estates. Supplementary feeding in winter, combined with low culling rates, has allowed deer numbers to rise in some areas, to the detriment of the habitat and the deer themselves. Increasing numbers have caused deer to move into sub-optimal habitats, and possibly increased the rate of mortality on roads and railways. In the last five years some grouse-moor estates have been reducing deer numbers because of the supposed risk of spreading disease-carrying ticks to red grouse. To protect pure red deer on islands where they have not been exposed to sika hybridisation, refuges have been designated on 6 islands, of which Rum is one. It is illegal to import sika to these islands, and the importation of red deer requires them to be genetically tested for purity.

Current distribution Red deer are widely distributed throughout mainland Highland, wherever extensive tracts of open ground or woodlands occur. They are absent from the more enclosed farmed areas of the Black Isle, Easter Ross and Caithness. Populations are present on Skye, Rum, Raasay and Scalpay. Red deer are good swimmers, and individuals may reach some of the closer offshore islands which are too small to support a permanent population. A stag was seen on Eigg in 1992, presumably having swum across from Rum.

Distributional trends The range of red deer appears approximately the same now as in the ITE Atlas.

Nature of records Three-quarters (74%) of records are of live sightings, with 20% identified from signs (tracks, droppings, cast antlers, wallows etc.) and the remainder found dead (mostly on the roads).

Where to look Red deer can be conspicuous not only in the rut but also in the winter when bad weather forces them onto lower ground including roadsides. Some estates and nature reserves now run deer watching and photographic safaris.

Fascinating fact On the island of Rum red deer have been observed biting the heads off Manx shearwater chicks and occasionally also chewing the shearwaters' legs and wings to reach bone (Furness,

1988). This is thought to be due to a deficiency of calcium in the local vegetation.

Red deer

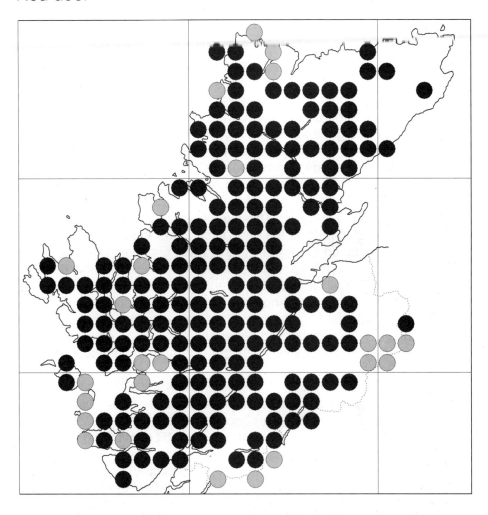

Grey dot = 1999 and before
Black dot = 2000 and after

Sika

Order: Artiodactyla
Cervus nippon Temminck 1838   Gaelic: fiadh lapanach
Synonym: sika deer or Japanese sika (the word sika means deer)

Conservation status W&C Act Schedule 9; WANE Act; Deer Scotland Act 1996 Close seasons (Scotland): Stags 21st October - 30th June; Hinds 16th February - 20th October.

Recognition and signs Sika are intermediate in size between red and roe deer. They are closely related to red deer and able to hybridise with them, giving rise to deer of variable size. Shoulder height for sika females (hinds) can be up to 1m and males (stags) up to 1.2m. Stags average 40kg in weight and hinds 31kg. The summer coat is chestnut or fawn, marked with distinct white spots. These are usually absent from the winter coat which is grey to almost black. In poor light sika can look black. Newly born calves range from chocolate to nearly yellow marked with white spots. One reliable identification feature is the white caudal patch outlined in black. This can be erected or flared in alarm. Another identification point is the pale patch under the chin and a small one, the hock gland, on the lower parts of both hind legs. Tracks resemble those of roe or yearling red deer. Droppings can also be confused with those of roe and young red deer. The stags have relatively simple antlers which normally develop up to only four points on each side, distinguishing them from the more complex antlers of red deer. In the field the high pitched penetrating whistle of the stags, especially during the rut or when they are disturbed, is an excellent identification point.

Ecology and Behaviour Sika can be difficult to see and if disturbed by, for example, shooting they can become almost nocturnal. They are also essentially woodland deer and have the habit of standing and just watching people and so go undetected. They are difficult to stalk compared with red deer. In the last two decades they, like roe deer, are increasingly seen in open areas such as moorland some distance from tree cover, particularly where they are undisturbed. Their life cycle is similar to that of red deer, with the rut in autumn and calving in spring. Sika stags wandering before the rut may find themselves in areas where there are red deer hinds but no sika hinds. This is thought to be how hybridisation has taken place, rather than by red deer stags mating with sika hinds (Senn & Pemberton, 2009).

History in Highland Sika are native to Japan. Their introduction to estates and deer parks for sport or amenity since the late 19th century has been fairly well documented. In Highland they were introduced at: Achanalt Forest near Garve (NH36) (1889); Rosehall (NC40) (end of 19th century); Glenmazeran () (1900); Aldourie Castle (NH63) (1900); Rosehaugh Estate (NH65) (1900); Coulin (NH05) (1919); Berriedale, (ND12) (1920); Loch Morar (NM79) (1920); and Knockie Castle, Loch Ness (date unknown) Not all of these populations persist. There are undoubtedly other introductions that have not been recorded.

Past and current management In the last two decades or so there has been a policy of culling sika deer wherever and whenever they are seen, to attempt to control hybridisation with red deer. However, after the first cross, hybrids may back-cross with either parent species, giving rise to offspring which may look like pure sika but have red deer genes and vice versa, making it very difficult for stalkers. To protect red deer on islands where they have not been exposed to sika hybridisation, refuges have been designated on six islands, of which Rum is one. It is illegal to import sika to these islands, and the importation of red deer requires them to be genetically tested for purity.

Current distribution The mainland distribution of sika reflects their spread from the original points of introduction. They have also been recorded from Skye – but their method of arrival there is not known. The distribution of pure sika may be blurred by the difficulty of identifying hybrids

Distributional trends Recorded from 69 Highland 10km squares in the ITE atlas compared to 52 now. No trend apparent.

Nature of records The majority of records (85%) are of live sightings with the remaining 15% divided equally between road casualties, shot animals and identification from signs.

Where to look Sika can be very difficult to see, but watching at dawn and dusk in places where there are good populations, such as the southern shore of Loch Ness between Inverness and Fort Augustus, offers your best chance.

Sika

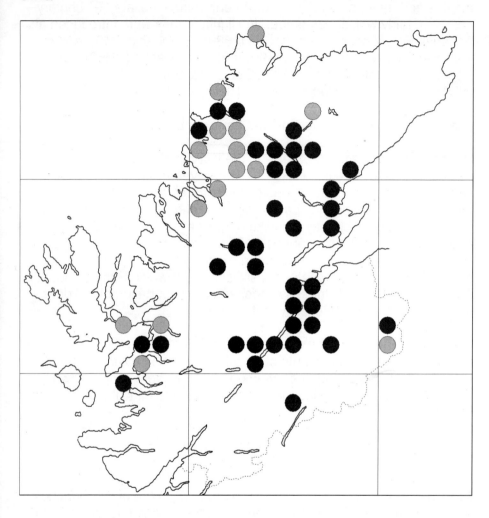

Grey dot = 1999 and before
Black dot = 2000 and after

Roe deer

Order: Artiodactyla
Capreolus capreolus (Linnaeus 1758)   Synonym: European roe deer
Gaelic: boc, boc-earba (buck); earb, eilid-earba (doe); meann, meann-earba (kid)

Conservation status Deer (Scotland) Act 1996 Close seasons
(Scotland): bucks 21st Oct - 31st March; does 1st April 1 20th October,
SBL (social criterion)

Recognition and signs Roe is the smallest native deer species in
Highland (but see muntjac). Males (bucks) are slightly larger than
females (does). Mean weight: bucks 25kg; does 23kg. Height at
shoulder: bucks about 70cm; does 60cm. The summer coat is a sleek
foxy red with a buff caudal patch. A white chin patch contrasts with the
black nose. The grey-brown winter coat, showing two white throat
patches, grows in September and October. The deer look scruffy whilst
in moult. The caudal patch is kidney-shaped in the buck and diamond-
shaped in the doe. In winter it appears whiter, in contrast with the
darker coat, and the doe has a downward-pointing tush of hair which
makes the caudal patch resemble the ace of spades. As with red, sika
and fallow the young (kids or fawns) have spotted coats for camouflage.
Only the bucks have antlers. These are roughened (pearled) near the
base and very short compared with those of other deer (see Plate IV).
Roe deer tracks are characterised by their small size and the narrow,
pointed shape of the hoofs, and also by the fact that the impression is
flat. In old animals the hoof tips are blunt. The track is about 4.5cms
long and the same size in both sexes. Roe deer droppings are 10-14
mm long and 7-10 mm across and are black or dark brown. In winter
they are short and cylindrical, sometimes almost spherical, often with
one end rounded and the other pointed. In summer the droppings are
frequently deposited in large clumps. When alarmed, roe deer make a
distinctive gruff bark which may be repeated several times. During the
rut, bucks make characteristic "rings" by circling around a tree or
sapling, which they may fray with their antlers.

Ecology and behaviour The roe deer was formerly almost entirely a
woodland species at home in both conifer and broadleaved woodland.
Whilst it is still common and widespread in woodland it has spread into
other areas such as open moorland and urban sites. The reason for
this change is not known. They are usually seen in small family units or

singly. In winter larger groups of up to 20 may congregate in suitable feeding areas such as field margins. Roe deer are selective feeders, choosing the more nutritious parts of plants. Unlike other deer, roe bucks cast their antlers between October and December, and may be seen growing new ones 'in velvet' until March. The velvet is shed in spring. Bucks begin to establish their territories as early as June, prior to the rut in July/August. Fighting between bucks is commonplace. Roe deer are the only hoofed animals in which the implantation of the fertilised eggs is delayed. Twin kids are common and triplets occasional. The doe leaves her young hidden in vegetation while she goes to feed, returning to suckle them periodically. Such kids are not abandoned and should be left well alone. The kids are weaned at 3 months and leave their mother's home range when about a year old. Mortality on roads is frequent and roe deer tend to get caught in wire fences more than other species. Predation by dogs of both adults and kids is increasing in woodland. Predation on tiny kids by golden eagle, fox and perhaps buzzards is significant.

History in Highland Roe deer have been present in Britain for 10,000 years, but their populations have fluctuated in response to human activities. Woodland clearance meant that they reached a low ebb in the 16th and 17th centuries, only recovering with the onset of estate forestry in the 18th century. They now seem to be recovering much of their lost range. Unlike red, sika or fallow deer they are very difficult to keep in parks, although an exception was the famous deer park at Rosehall (NC40) in Sutherland, which in 1923 contained 150 red, 200 fallow, 50 sika and 40 roe deer.

Past and current management Roe deer continue to be managed for sport, and to control the damage they do to trees and shrubs. Although roe deer venison is not popular in Britain, it is considered a delicacy in Europe, and attracts a high price. Roe buck stalking for "trophy" heads is renowned by stalkers from all over the world.

Current distribution Roe deer are widespread across the Highland mainland and on Skye. There is one record of signs from Tanera Mor in 2006 - possibly an animal had swum across from the mainland? Berry (1983) and the ITE Atlas report them from Raasay, but we have no records. The map shows large gaps in the flow country of mid and west Sutherland and parts of Caithness. They are becoming more frequent in urban situations (gardens, parks and burial grounds), in Inverness.

Distributional trends The distribution now is very similar to that shown in the ITE Atlas.

Nature of records The majority of records (64%) are of live sightings, with road (and other) casualties 21% and identification from signs 15%.

Fascinating fact When alarmed the caudal patch is made more conspicuous by raising the hairs called 'flaring'. The animal may also bound along leaping clear off the ground, which is known as 'pronking'.

Roe deer   Grey dot = 1999 and before   Black dot = 2000 and after

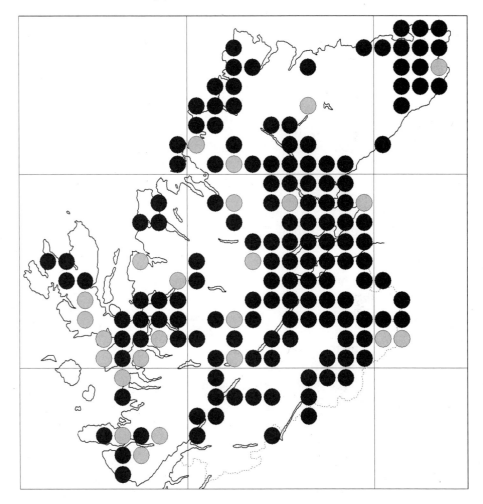

Feral goat

Order: Artiodactyla

Capra hircus Linnaeus 1758

Synonym: wild goat

Gaelic: gobhar, gobhar fiadhaich; boc, boc-gobhair (billy); meann, meann-gobhair (kid)

Conservation status None

Recognition and signs Unlikely to be confused with any other British mammal. Similar to a domestic goat but with a long shaggy coat. The colour of the adults varies from white through to almost back. Silvery coats are not uncommon but most goats are grey, brown or black with pale patches. Both sexes have horns. The males' (billies) horns may grow to 76 cm and the annual growth 'ridges' can be used to age them. Billies exhibit two distinct forms of horns, one almost parallel and the other markedly diverging. The first is reputed to be inherited from the Spanish ibex and the other from the Grecian ibex. Both sexes have beards and have flat long tails that are bare underneath. Billies are around 70 cm at the shoulder and weigh around 65 kg. Young billies are difficult to tell from nannies (females). The smell of the billies in rut, starting in mid-August, is unique! Droppings are cylindrical about 1 cm long and sometimes flattened at one or both ends. They often lie in small heaps. Tracks show the hoofs being rounded at the tips and narrower in front than behind. Tips are often very widely splayed and each half of the hoof has a convex outer margin and a concave inner margin. Goats are surprisingly non vocal, but when alarmed they may snort. The distress call is a loud wavering scream.

Ecology and Behaviour The ability of goats to exploit almost any type of food means they can be found in a wide range of habitats. They are equally at home on steep cliffs, inland or coastal, and open moorland if there is some woodland for shelter. They were formerly known as the 'poor man's cow' as they could eat natural food from grass to bark and gorse and did not require supplementary food like domestic stock. Their loose gatherings are known as tribes. For most of the year the older billies live apart from the nannies, kids and young billies. The home range of the nannies is constant but billies tend to roam over large areas of ground particularly in the rut. The kids are born in January or February and twins are not uncommon. The kids are often hidden for the first few days and may be preyed on by golden eagles and foxes.

126

History in Highland Goats are native to the Middle East, and are thought to have come to Britain with the first farmers, during the Neolithic period. They have been moved around by people ever since. They reached their greatest numbers in the highlands during the late 18th century when some parishes held over 1,000 feral or wild goats. They survived on their own, but supplied meat, milk, hides and even horns for many people. After the clearances goats were less likely to be tolerated by the now landlords. The two World Wars saw a marked decrease as goats were shot for food.

Past and current management Goats have had mixed fortunes recently, having been shot out in some areas but introduced into others for sport. Stalkers are reputed to pay £1,000 for a trophy billy. In some areas goats have been subjected to heavy culling in order to permit forestry planting or woodland regeneration. Elsewhere they are persecuted because of the supposed spread of disease-carrying ticks from goats to red grouse. There are probably fewer goats in Highland now than there have been for centuries.

Current distribution Some tribes of goats are still found at historical sites such as the Rogart area (NC70), An Teallach (NH09) and Kintail (NG91). They have gone, having been shot out, from such places as Inverpolly (NC11) and Moy (NH73). Among the islands, they are found on Rum, and previously occurred on Canna and Eigg. Their status on Skye is uncertain as both records were of dead carcases on west-facing beaches. These carcases could have floated across from Rum.

Nature of records The vast majority of records (95%) are of live sightings, as goats can be conspicuous in most of the habitats they frequent. The remaining 5% of records were road or other casualties.

Distributional trends Recorded from 41 Highland 10km squares in the ITE atlas compared to 35 now. This possibly represents a genuine decrease in range, as several goat tribes are known to have been extirpated recently. The decrease is even more marked when compared with the distribution given in the classic monograph by Whitehead (1972).

Where to look Some sites are easily seen from the road, as at Kintail (NG91) or Dundonnell (NH08). Those on the south side of Loch Ness may be seen from tourist boats on the Loch. Goats may also be seen on the island of Rum National Nature Reserve.

Fascinating fact In the heyday of the Highland goat in the late 18th century, large numbers of cattle were being taken south by the celebrated 'drovers'. Other drovers were bringing goats in from Ireland in considerable numbers and taking them north. As they went, some goats escaped on the way, but the remainder managed to reach the northern parts of Caithness and Sutherland.

Feral goat   Grey dot = 1999 and before   Black dot = 2000 and after

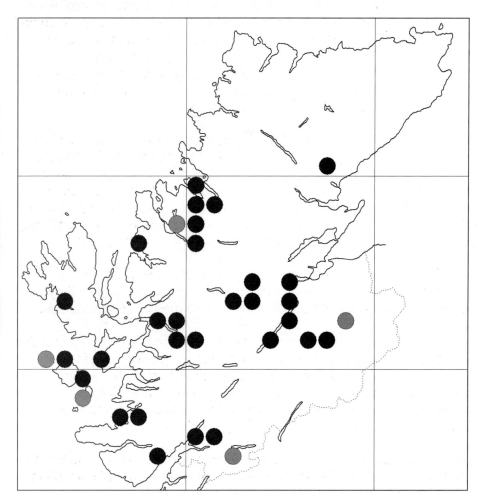

Escapes, semi-domestic, vagrants and unconfirmed

Various other species have been recorded, or have been suspected of occurring without definite records, in Highland over the years. These fall into the four categories described below.

Escapes from captivity Many different species have been kept captive for one reason or another over the years – for fur farming, as exotic pets, or in wildlife parks. Inevitably escapes occur. The inception of the Dangerous Wild Animals Act in 1976, which required certain exotic species to be licensed if kept in captivity, is often cited as a reason why a spate of such animals was reported shortly afterwards. The only really likely Highland candidate for this explanation is Felicity the **puma** (*Puma concolor*). She was captured alive near Cannich (NH33) in 1980, and lived out her days at the Highland Wildlife Park, achieving further fame after death as a mounted exhibit in Inverness Museum.

The ITE Atlas records a **muskrat** (*Ondatra zibethicus*) from North Kessock (NH64). This species was imported for fur farming in the 1920s and soon escaped to establish feral populations. These were eliminated, as being potentially damaging to agriculture, in the 1930s.

An **Arctic fox** (*Alopex lagopus*) recorded in the hills above Drumnadrochit (NH43) in the 1980s may have originated from any of the above sources, whilst a **raccoon** (*Procyon lotor*) killed on the A9 at North Kessock (NH64) in 2005 had most likely escaped from a local wildlife park.

There were several reported **muntjac** (*Muntiacus reevesii*) sightings from East Inverness-shire in the 1980s and 1990s, and one from the Black Isle in 2000. As yet, none has been authenticated by a photograph or carcase. These small deer, originating in China, are well-established in England where they cause considerable damage to native woodlands and gardens. One juvenile is known to have escaped from a former wildlife park near Beauly (NH44) in the 1980s. Others may have been released when this establishment eventually closed down. Muntjac are smaller than roe deer and, when at low densities, keep well hidden in dense cover. They may also be less vocal (an alternative name is 'barking deer') when the population is small. So it is not inconceivable that they are present. Scottish Natural Heritage has recently published a report on the potential costs of keeping them out of Scotland (Ward & Lees, 2011).

Captive or semi-domestic Some species are on the borderline between wildness and domesticity, living in semi-natural habitats but being to some extent looked after by people. The Cairngorm **reindeer** (*Rangifer tarandus*) herd falls into this category. Whilst they are free-ranging over the slopes of Cairngorm (NH90), the ancestors of the current herd were brought here from Sweden during the 1950s. They are given supplementary feed, and some of their number are even called upon to pull Santa's sleigh at Christmas.

Native to Anatolia, **fallow deer** (*Dama dama*) were originally brought to Britain by the Normans as park deer, but soon spread more widely in England. Their only occurrences in Highland are within deer parks or other enclosures. Whitehead (1964) lists many sites in Highland where they were introduced. However, he also records the demise of many of these populations. In 1950 there were four deer parks in Highland with fallow deer: at Berriedale, Caithness (ND12); Dunrobin, Sutherland (NC80); Garve north of Inverness (NH36); and Aldourie (NH63) at the north east end of Loch Ness. A former deer park at Rosehall, Sutherland (NC40), was disbanded during World War 2. The ITE Atlas gives post-1960 records for NH35, NH36 and NH45. The only positive recent records are from: Berriedale (ND12), where there is still a small herd of white fallow deer in a park; Ardnamurchan (NM56) where they have recently been introduced to a privately-owned forestry plantation; and Morar (NM69) where they were observed within a fenced enclosure in 2009.

Vagrants Various species beyond the limits of their normal range turn up in Highland periodically. The most recent notable visitor was a magnificent **bearded seal** (*Erignathus barbatus*) (see Plate IV) which was seen in the Inverness Firth (NH64, NH75) several times during November 2007. This species normally lives in Arctic waters, but has been recorded several times in Orkney and Shetland, as well as further down the east coast of England. Two were also seen together off Skye in 1999. Another infrequent Arctic visitor is the **harp seal** (*Pagophilus groenlandica*) or **Greenland seal**. This highly mobile species normally lives in the Arctic Atlantic, breeding in on ice floes and feeding on pelagic fish and crustaceans. Occasionally they move further south into the North Sea and are seen off the British coast. Harvie-Brown and Buckley (1887) report that one was killed by a Mr Houston at Kintradwell (NC90) before 1870, and that a specimen in Dunrobin museum is a young harp seal (although where it came from is not mentioned). One was also taken on the west coast, in Loch Nedd in Assynt (NC13) by three lobster fishermen 'on the last day of December 1903' (Way, 1905). Harvie-Brown and MacPherson (1904) Report that a **walrus** (*Odobenus rosmarus*) was seen in 1887 near Stein (Skye) (NG25) and later off Sleat and possibly Eigg. Neither of these species has been reported more recently.

Unconfirmed Despite many reports in the press and other media over the years, there have been no authenticated records of free-living **'big cats'** in Highland (except for Felicity the puma). We await developments.

Once and future Eurasian **beavers** (*Castor fiber*) have already been reintroduced to Scotland, on a trial basis, in Knapdale, Argyll. The European Habitats Directive empowers Governments to consider reintroducing extinct native species. Other potential candidates to enrich our future mammal fauna are the **lynx** (*Lynx lynx*) and the **wolf** (*Canis lupus*).

References

Altringham, J (2003) *British Bats.* The New Naturalist, HarperCollins, London.

Arnold, HR (1993) *Atlas of mammals in Britain.* ITE research publication no. 6. Natural Environment Research Council. HMSO, London.

Balharry, D (1993) Factors affecting the distribution and population density of pine martens (*Martes martes* L.) in Scotland. PhD Thesis, University of Aberdeen.

Balharry, D (1999) *How to exclude pine martens from game and poultry pens.* The Vincent Wildlife Trust, London.

Balharry, EA, McGowan, GM, Kruuk, H and Halliwell, E (1996) *Distribution of pine martens in Scotland as determined by field survey and questionnaire.* Scottish Natural Heritage Research, Survey and Monitoring Report No. 48.

Barlow, KE (1997) *The diets of two phonic types of the bat Pipistrellus pipistrellus in Britain.* Journal of Zoology, London 243, 579-609. In Racey, PA, Raynor, R and Pritchard, S (2004) (Eds.) *A review of European Bat Lyssavirus (EBLV) and the status of bats in Scotland.* Scottish Natural Heritage Commissioned Report No. 063.

Barrett-Hamilton, GEH and Hinton, MAC (1911-1921) *A history of British mammals.* Gurney and Jackson, London.

Battersby, J. (Ed) & Tracking Mammals Partnership (2005). UK Mammals: Species Status and Population Trends. First Report by the Tracking Mammals Partnership. JNCC/Tracking Mammals Partnership, Peterborough.

Bell, B (2007) The rat eradication programme on Canna. Proceedings of a Conference 'Tackling the problem of invasive alien mammals on seabird colonies' held in September 2007 at Edinburgh Zoo.

Berry, RJ (1970) The Natural history of the House mouse. Field Studies 3 (2), 219-262.

Berry, RJ (1983) *Evolution of animals and plants.* pp. 433-447 in: Boyd, JM and Bowes, DR (Eds.) *The Natural Environment of the Inner Hebrides.* Proceedings of the Royal Society of Edinburgh B 83, 1-648.

Berry, RJ (1996) Small mammal differentiation on islands. *Phil. Trans. Roy. Soc. B.* 351, 753-764.

Berry, RJ (2000). *Orkney Nature.* T & AD Poyser, London.

Berry, RJ (2009) *Islands.* New Naturalist No. 109, HarperCollins, London.

Birks, JDS (2006) An artificial natal den box for pine martens (*Martes martes*). In: Santos-Reis, M *et al.,* (Eds.) *Martes* in Carnivore Communities. Alpha Wildlife Publications, Sherwood Park, Alberta, Canada.

Birks, JDS (2008) *The Polecat Survey of Britain 2004-2006.* The Vincent Wildlife Trust, Ledbury.

Briggs, B. & King, D. (1998). *The Bat Detective: A Field Guide for Bat Detection.* Stag Electronics.

Brown, H and Birks, JDS (2006) Resolving conflicts generated by pine martens' (*Martes martes*) denning in buildings in Scotland. In: Santos-Reis, M *et al.,*(Eds.) *Martes* in Carnivore Communities. Alpha Wildlife Publications, Sherwood Park, Alberta, Canada.

131

Buckley TE & Harvie-Brown JA (1884) *The Vertebrate Fauna of Sutherlandshire.* David Douglas, Edinburgh.

Campbell, JL (1984) *Canna the Story of a Hebridean Island.* Oxford University Press, Oxford.

Canham, M (1992). A brown long-eared bat maternity roost in Sutherland. *Scottish Bats*, Vol. 1. South-east Scotland Bat Groups.

Carter, P and Churchfield, S (2006) *Distribution and habitat occurrence of water shrews in Great Britain.* Environment Agency, Bristol.

Catania, KC, Hare, JF, and Campbell, KL (2008) Water shrews detect movement, shape, and smell to find prey underwater. Proceedings of the National Academy of Sciences 105(2), 571-576.

Clark, H & Sellers, RM (2005) *The Birds and Mammals of Caithness: Robert Innes Shearer's contributions to the natural history of Caithness, 1859-1867.* Bellfield Publications, Wick.

Clode, D and Macdonald DW (1995) Evidence for food competition between mink (*Mustela vison*) and otter (*Lutra lutra*) on Scottish Islands. Journal of Zoology, 237, 435-444.

Clutton-Brock. TH, Guinness, FE and Albon, SD (1982) *Red Deer: Behaviour and Ecology of two sexes.* Edinburgh University Press.

Collier, RV and McGhie, HA (2003) Persecution of the red squirrel by the Highland Squirrel Club 1903-1946. Scottish Naturalist, 115, 39-61.

Corbet, GB (1979) Small mammals above the tree-line in the Cairngorms. Unpublished report.

Craik, C (1997) Long-term effects of North American Mink *Mustela vison* on seabirds in western Scotland. Bird Study 44, 303-309.

Cuthbert, JH (1973) The origin and distribution of feral mink in Scotland. Mammal Review 3 (3), 97-103.

Darling FF (1947) *Natural History in the Highlands and Islands.* Collins, London.

Darling, FF and Boyd, JM (1964) *The Highlands and Islands.* Collins, London.

Davis, AR & Gray, D (2010) The distribution of Scottish wildcats (*Felis silvestris*) in Scotland (2006-2008). Scottish Natural Heritage Commissioned Report No. 360.

Davison, A, Birks, JDS, Brookes, RC, Braithwaite, TC and Messenger, JE (2002) On the origin of faeces: morphological *versus* molecular methods for surveying rare carnivores from their scats. Journal of Zoology 257(2), 141-143.

Delany, M.J. (1961) The ecological distribution of small mammals in North-West Scotland. *Proc. zool. Soc. Lond.* 137, 107-126.

Delany, MJ and Bishop, IR (1960) The systematics, life history and evolution of the bank-vole *Clethrionomys* Tilesius in North-West Scotland. *Proc. zool. Soc. Lond.* 135, 409-422.

Dietz, C, Helversen, O and Nill, D (2009). *Bats of Britain, Europe and Northwest Africa.* A & C Black.

Driscoll, CA, Menotti-Raymond, M, Roca, AL, Hupe, K, Johnson, WE, Geffen, E, Harley, EH, Delibes, M, Pontier, D, Kitchener, AC, Yamaguchi, N, O'Brien, SJ, Macdonald, DW (2007) The Near Eastern Origin of Cat Domestication. Science 317, 519-523.

Easterbee, N, Hepburn, LV and Jefferies, DJ (1991) *Survey of the status and distribution of the wildcat in Scotland 1983-1987.* Nature Conservancy Council for Scotland, Edinburgh.

Fisher, DO, Lambin, X and Yletyinen, SM (2009) Experimental translocation of juvenile water voles in a Scottish lowland metapopulation. Population Ecology, 00, 289-295.

Furness, RW (1988) Predation on ground-nesting seabirds by island populations of red deer *Cervus elaphus* and sheep *Ovis*. Journal of Zoology 216, 565–573.

Glover, AM & Altringham, JD (2008) Cave selection and use by swarming bat species. Biological Conservation, 141, 1493-1504.

Green, J & Green, R (1980) *Otter survey of Scotland 1977-79.* The Vincent Wildlife Trust, London.

Gurnell, J, Lurz, P & Pepper, H (2001) Practical techniques for surveying and monitoring squirrels. Forestry Commission Practice Note.

Haddow, J (1992) Recorded distribution of bats in Scotland. *Scottish Bats*, Vol. 1. South-east Scotland Bat Groups.

Halliwell, EC (1997) The ecology of red squirrels in Scotland in relation to pine marten predation. PhD thesis, University of Aberdeen.

Harrington, LA, Hughes, J and Macdonald DW (2008) Management of American mink in the northern highlands: a proposed *cordon sanitaire* approach. Wildlife Conservation Research Unit (WildCRU), University of Oxford.

Harris S & Yalden, DW (2008) *Mammals of the British Isles: Handbook, 4th Edition.* The Mammal Society, Southampton.

Harvie-Brown, JA (1892) *A Vertebrate Fauna of Argyll and the Inner Hebrides.* David Douglas, Edinburgh.

Harvie-Brown JA (1895) *A Vertebrate Fauna of the Moray Basin.* David Douglas, Edinburgh.

Harvie-Brown JA & Buckley TE (1897) *A Vertebrate Fauna of Sutherland, Caithness and West Cromarty.* David Douglas, Edinburgh.

Harvie-Brown JA & MacPherson Rev. HA (1904) *A Vertebrate Fauna of the North-west Highlands and Skye.* David Douglas, Edinburgh.

Hewson, R (1990) Victim of Myth. A report to the League Against Cruel Sports, London.

Hull, R (2007) *Scottish Mammals.* Birlinn Ltd., Edinburgh.

Institute of Ecology and Environmental Management [IEEM], (2009). *Guidance on Metadata Standards: Reporting, Sharing and Archiving Ecological Data.* Professional Guidance Series 14.

Jackson, DB and Green, RE (2000) The importance of the introduced hedgehog (*Erinaceus europaeus*) as a predator of the eggs of waders (Charadrii) on machair in South Uist, Scotland. Biological Conservation 93 (3), 333-348.

Kinrade, V, Ewald, J, Smith, A, Newey, S, Iason, G, Thirgood, S & Raynor, R (2008) The distribution of Mountain Hare (*Lepus timidus*) in Scotland (206/07). Scottish Natural Heritage Commissioned Report No. 278.

Kitchener, AC, Yamaguchi, N, Ward, JM, and Macdonald, DW (2005) A diagnosis for the Scottish wildcat (*Felis silvestris*): a tool for conservation action for a critically-endangered felid. Animal Conservation 8, 223-237.

Kolb HH (1986) Some observations on the home range of vixens (*Vulpes vulpes*) in the suburbs of Edinburgh. Journal of Zoology 210A, 636-639.

Kruuk H (1989) *The Social Badger*. Oxford University Press, Oxford.

Lambert, RA (2002) The grey seal in Britain: a twentieth century history of a nature conservation success. Environment and History 8, 449-474.

Lambin, X, Aars, J, Piertney, SB & Telfer, S (2004) Inferring pattern and process in small mammal metapopulations: insights from ecological and genetic data. pp. 515-450 in: Hanski I & Eilpin M (Eds.) Ecology, Genetics and Evolution of Metapopulations. Elsevier, Inc.

Lambin, X, Le Bouille, D, Oliver, MK, Sutherland, C, Tedesco, E, Douglas, A (In Press) High connectivity despite high fragmentation: iterated dispersal in a vertebrate.

Langley, PJW and Yalden, DW (1977) The decline of the rarer carnivores in Great Britain during the nineteenth century. Mammal Review 7(3/4), 95-116.

Laurenson, MK, Norman, RA, Gilbert, L, Reid, HW, & Hudson, PJ (2003) Identifying disease reservoirs in complex systems: mountain hares as reservoirs of ticks and louping-ill virus, pathogens of red grouse. Journal of Animal Ecology 72, 177-185.

Lawson, TJ (Ed.) (1995) *The Quaternary of Assynt and Coigach. Field Guide.* Cambridge: Quaternary Research Association.

Levi, P (Ed.) (1984) Samuel Johnson's 'A Journey to the Western Islands of Scotland' (1775) and James Boswell's 'The Journal of a Tour to the Hebrides' (1786). Penguin Classics.

Lockie, JD (1964) The breeding density of the golden eagle and fox in relation to food supply in Wester Ross, Scotland. Scottish Naturalist 71, 67-77.

Macdonald, DW, Daniels, MJ, Driscoll, C. Kitchener, A and Yamaguchi, N (2004) The Scottish Wildcat Analyses for Conservation and an Action Plan. WildCRU, Oxford.

MacNally, L (1968) Highland Year. Dent, London.

Martin, M (1695) A Description of The Western Islands Of Scotland.

McGhie, H (2002) Changes in distribution and persecution of carnivores in north Scotland 1912-1970, as evidenced by taxidermists' records. The Scottish Naturalist 114, 45-83.

Miller, H (1854) *My Schools and Schoolmasters.* Morrison & Gibb, Edinburgh.

Mortimer, N. (1995). Pipistrelles in a sea cave. *Scottish Bats*, Vol. 3.

Mulville, J (2010) Red deer on Scottish Islands. Chapter 6 in O'Connor, T & Sykes, N (Eds.) Extinctions and Invasions – A Social history of British Fauna. Windgather Press, Oxford.

Patterson, D & Wells, L (2008) Pine Woodland Bat Survey – North Highland (2006-2008). North Highland Bat Network. Unpublished report submitted to *Scottish Bats*.

Pennant, T (1777) *Caledonian Zoology*.

Piertney, S, Stewart, WA, Lambin, X, Telfer, S, Aars, J, & Dallas, JF (2005) Phylogeographic structure and postglacial evolutionary history of water voles (*Arvicola terrestris*) in the United Kingdom. Molecular Ecology, 14, 1435-1444.

Racey, PA, Raynor, R & Pritchard, S (2004) (Eds.) *A review of European Bat Lyssavirus (EBLV) and the status of bats in Scotland*. Scottish Natural Heritage Commissioned Report No. 063.

Rainey, E, Butler, A, Bierman, S & Roberts, AMI (2009) Scottish Badger Distribution Survey 2006 – 2009; estimating the distribution and density of badger main setts in Scotland. Report prepared by Scottish Badgers and Biomathematics and Statistics Scotland.

Richardson, P (2000) *Distribution atlas of bats in Britain and Ireland 1980-1999*. The Bat Conservation Trust.

Ritchie, J (1920) *The influence of man on animal life in Scotland*. Cambridge University Press, Cambridge.

Ryland. K & Kemp, B. (2009) Identifying voles from their field signs. British Wildlife, 20(5), 330-334.

Scott, R, Easterbee, N and Jefferies, DJ (1993) A radio-tracking study of wildcats in western Scotland. pp. 94-97 in: Seminar on the biology and conservation of the wildcat (Felis silvestris). Environmental Encounters No. 16, Council of Europe Press, Strasbourg.

Scottish Natural Heritage and Forestry Commission Scotland (2011) Conserving Scotland's Red Squirrels.

Searle, JB, Kotlik, P, Rambau, RV, Markova, S, Herman, JS & McDevitt, AD (2009) The Celtic fringe of Britain: insights from small mammal phylogeography. Proceedings of the Royal Society B, 276, 4287-4294.

Searle, JB, Jones, CS, Gündüz, I, Scascitelli, M, Jones, EP, Herman, JS, Rambau, V, Noble, LR, Berry, RJ, Giménez, MD and Jóhannesdóttir, F (2009) Of mice and (Viking?) men: phylogeography of British and Irish house mice. Proceedings of the Royal Society B 276, 201-207.

Senn, HV & Pemberton, JM (2009) Variable extent of hybridization between invasive sika (*Cervus nippon*) and native red deer (*C. elaphus*) in a small geographical area. Molecular Ecology 18, 862–876.

Solow, AR, Kitchener, AC, Robert, DL and Birks, JSD (2006) Rediscovery of the Scottish polecat, *Mustela putorius*: Survival or reintroduction? Biological Conservation 128, 574–575.

Stoneman, J & Zonfrillo, B (2005) The eradication of Brown Rats from Handa Island, Sutherland. Scottish Birds 25, 17-23.

Strachan, R & Moorhouse, T (2006) *Water Vole Conservation Handbook*. Wildlife Conservation Research Unit, Oxford.

Swift, SM (1998) *Long-eared Bats*. T & AD Poyser, London.

Swift, S, Boag, B, Armstrong, J & Armstrong, S (2001) Relative abundance of 45 and 55 kHz pipistrelle bats in Perth and Kinross and Clackmannanshire. Unpublished Report to SNH.

Thompson, PM, McConnell, BJ, Tollit, DJ, Mackay, A, Hunter, C & Racey, PA (1996). Comparative distribution, movements and diet of harbour and grey seals from the Moray Firth, N.E. Scotland. Journal of Applied Ecology, 33: 1572-1584.

Thorburn, A (1974) *Thorburn's Mammals.* Ebury Press & Michael Joseph, London. [In Hull, R. (2007). *Scottish Mammals.* Birlinn Ltd., Edinburgh].

Thorpe, A (2001) North Sea Bird Club: 21st Anniversary Report.

Van Parijs, SM, Corkeron, PJ, Harvey, J, Hayes, S, Mellinger, D, Rouget, P, Thompson, PM, Wahlberg, M & Kovacs, KM (2003) Patterns in vocalizations of male harbor seals. Journal of the Acoustic Society of America, 113, 3403-3410.

Ward, Al & Lees, K (2011) Analysis of cost of preventing establishment in Scotland of muntjac deer (*Muntiacus spp.*). Scottish Natural Heritage Commissioned Report No. 457.

Way, JP (1905) Greenland seal taken in Sutherlandshire. *Ann. Scottish Nat. Hist. 1905.* 181.

Webbon, CC et al (2004) Faecal density counts for monitoring changes in red fox numbers in rural Britain. Journal of Applied Ecology 41, 768-779.

Wells, L. (2010). *Assynt Cave Bat Project – Progress Report 2009.* North Highland Bat Network. Unpublished report, January 2010.

Wells, L & Patterson, D (2005). *Bats in Bridges Survey – East Sutherland Area.* North Highland Bat Network. Unpublished report submitted to *Scottish Bats.*

Whitaker, S (1995) *Natural Heritage Interest of Road Verges and Bridges in Highland Region.* A pilot study report submitted to Highland Regional Council – Department of Roads and Transport. Scottish Natural Heritage, NW Region.

Whitehead, GK (1964) The Deer of Great Britain and Ireland. Routledge & Kegan Paul.

Williamson, GR (1988) Seals in Loch Ness. Scientific Reports of the Whales Research Institute, 39, 151-157.

Woodroffe, G (2000) *The water vole.* The Mammal Society, London.

Yalden, DW (1999) *The history of British Mammals.* T & AD Poyser, London.

Yoxon, G. M. (1992). Bats on Skye. *Scottish Bats*, Vol 1. South-east Scotland Bat Groups.

Yoxon, G. M. (1993). Bats confirmed on the Isle of Canna. *Scottish Bats,* Vol 2.

Further reading

All species:

Encyclopaedic - Harris S. & Yalden, D. W. (2008). *Mammals of the British Isles: Handbook, 4th Edition.* The Mammal Society, Southampton.

Introductory – Bullion, S (1998) *Key to British Land Mammals.* Field Studies Council laminated chart.
Bullion, S (2001) *A Guide to British Mammal Track and Signs.* Field Studies Council laminated chart.
Collier RV (1992) *Scottish Wildlife - Animals.* Colin Baxter Photography.
Macdonald DW & Barrett P (1999) *Collins Field Guide - Mammals of Britain and Europe.* HarperCollins, London.
Sargent, G & Morris, P (2003) *How to Find & Identify Mammals.* The Mammal Society, London.
Strachan, R (2010) *Mammal Detective* (2nd edition). Whittet Books, London.
Wembridge, D & Bowen, CP (2010) *Britain's Mammals a concise guide.* Whittet Books for the People's Trust for Endangered Species.

Audio - British Mammals an Audio Introduction: CD of mammal sounds (2009) British Library Sound Archive.

Rodents:
Flowerdew, J (1984) *Woodmice.* Anthony Nelson, Oswestry.
Gurnell, J (1994) *The Red Squirrel.* The Mammal Society, London.
Holm, J (2009) *Squirrels* (2nd edition). Whittet Books, London.
Lurz, P (2010) *Red Squirrels Naturally Scottish.* SNH Publications, Perth.
Woodroffe, G (2000) *The Water Vole.* The Mammal Society, London.

Lagomorphs:
McBride, A (2003) *Rabbits and Hares.* Whittet Books, London.
Tapper,R & Yalden,D (2010) *The Brown Hare.* The Mammal Society, Southampton.

Insectivores:
Carter, P and Churchfield, S (2009) *The Water Shrew Handbook.* The Mammal Society, Southampton.
Churchfield, S (1990) *The Natural History of Shrews.* Christopher Helm, London.
Gorman, ML and Stone, RD (1990) *The Natural History of Moles.* Christopher Helm, London.
Morris P (1994) *The Hedgehog.* The Mammal Society, London.
Morris, P (2010) *The New Hedgehog Book* (2nd edition). Whittet Books, London.
Reeve, N (1994) *Hedgehogs.* T & AD Poyser, London.
Stone, D (1986) *Moles.* Anthony Nelson, Oswestry.

137

Bats:
Jones, K & Walsh, A (2001) *A Guide to British Bats.* Field Studies Council laminated chart.
Waters, D & Waters, R (2009) *Bats.* The Mammal Society, Southampton.

Carnivores:
Anon. (1993) *The Polecat.* Vincent Wildlife Trust, London.
Birks, J (1986) *Mink.* Anthony Nelson, Oswestry.
Birks, J (2002) *The Pine Marten.* The Mammal Society, London.
Clark, M (2010) *Badgers.* Whittet Books, London.
Cooper, M & Ralston, J (1997) *Badgers Naturally Scottish.* SNH Publications, Perth.
Dunstone, N (1993) *The Mink.* T & AD Poyser, London.
Harris, S & White, P (1994) *The Red Fox.* The Mammal Society, London.
Kilshaw, K (2011) *Scottish Wildcats Naturally Scottish.* SNH Publications, Perth.
Kitchener, A (1995) *The Wildcat.* The Mammal Society, London.
Kruuk, H (1995) *Wild Otters Predation and Populations.* Oxford University Press, Oxford.
Macdonald DW (1987) *Running with the Fox.* Unwin Hyman, London.
McDonald, R and Harris, S (1998) *Stoats and Weasels.* The Mammal Society, London.
Sleeman, P (1989) *Stoats & Weasels, Polecats & Martens.* Whittet Books, London.
Woodroffe, G (2007) *The Otter.* The Mammal Society, Southampton.
Woods, M (2010) *The Badger.* The Mammal Society, Southampton.

Seals:
Anderson, S (1990) *Seals.* Whittet Books, London.
Duck, C (2007) *Seals Naturally Scottish.* SNH Publications, Perth.
Thompson, P (1989) *The Common Seal.* Shire Natural History, Aylesbury.

Ungulates:
Chapman, D & N (1997) *Fallow Deer.* Coch-Y-Bonddu Books.
Clutton-Brock, TH, & Albon, SD (1989) *Red Deer in the Highlands.* Blackwell, Oxford.
Putman, R (2000) *Sika Deer.* The Mammal Society & British Deer Society.
Whitehead GK (1993) *Encyclopedia of Deer.* Swan Hill Press.
Whitehead GK (1960) *The Deer Stalking Grounds of Great Britain and Ireland.* Hollis and Carter.
Whitehead, GK (1972) *The Wild Goats of Great Britain and Ireland.* David and Charles.

Useful organisations and websites

All Species:

The Mammal Society, 3 The Carronades, New Road, Southampton, SO140AA. The only membership organisation dedicated to the study and conservation of all mammals of the British Isles.   www.mammal.org

Scottish Natural Heritage www.snh.gov.uk
Many pages of information, advice and downloads on the conservation of Scotland's mammals. Includes information on the Scottish Biodiversity List and UK Biodiversity Action Plan species and SNH's Species Action Framework.

National Biodiversity Network Gateway http://data.nbn.org.uk
See the HBRG mammal dataset alongside many others.

Viewing facilities:

Wild Scotland www.wild-scotland.org.uk
Association of Scottish wildlife tourism operators

Highland Wildlife Park www.highlandwildlifepark.org
The easy way to see Scotland's mammals, plus long-extinct species in captivity

Forestry Commission www.forestry.gov.uk/ for information on the hides at Kylerhea and Garbh Eilean (Ardery) on Loch Sunart.

Strathspey Badger Hide www.highlandbadgers.net

Rodents: Rat eradication on Canna www.ntsseabirds.org.uk
Red Squirrels of the Highlands project www.redsquirrelsofthehighlands.co.uk

Bats: Bat Conservation Trust, Scottish Officer, Unit 10, RFL House, Anderson Street, Dunblane, FK15 9AJ   www.bats.org.uk/pages/bctscotland.html
Many useful downloads including: *Bat Surveys - Good Practice Guidelines*; *Building, Planning and Development*; and *Woodland Management for Bats.*

Carnivores: Cairngorms Wildcat Project www.highlandtiger.com
International Otter Survival Fund www.otter.org
Scottish Badgers www.scottishbadgers.org.uk
Scottish Mink Initiative www.scottishmink.org.uk
Scottish Wildcat Association www.scottishwildcats.co.uk

Seals: Dolphin & Seal Centre, N Kessock
www.highland.gov.uk/leisureandtourism/what-to-see/visitorcentres/northkessockdolphinandsealcentre.htm

Ungulates: British Deer Society: www.bds.org.uk
Cairngorm Reindeer herd www.cairngormreindeer.co.uk

Index of Species

Alopex lagopus 129
American mink 105–7, Plate II
Apodemus sylvaticus 15, 25–7
arctic fox 129
*Arvicola amphibius see Arvicola
    terrestris*
Arvicola terrestris 18, 21–4

badger 85–7, Plates III, IV
bats 58
    bandit pipistrelle (*see* common
        pipistrelle)
    brown long-eared bat 74–7
    common pipistrelle 66–9
    Daubenton's bat 59–61, 62
    Nathusius' pipistrelle 72
    Natterer's bat 62–3
    Noctule 64–5
    pipistrelles (undifferentiated) 68,
        69
    red-armed bat (*see* Natterer's
        bat)
    soprano pipistrelle 66, 68, 70–3
    water bat (*see* Daubenton's bat)
beaver 130
'big cats' 130
boar, wild *see* wild boar

Canis lupus 130
Canis vulpes see Vulpes vulpes
Capra hircus 126–8
Capreolus capreolus 123–5
cats
    feral cat 78–81
    wild cat 78–81
Cervus elaphus 116–19
Cervus nippon 116, 118, 120–2
*Clethrionomys glareolus see
    Myodes glareolus*
common rat *see* brown rat

coney *see* rabbit

Dama dama 130
deer
    European roe deer (*see* roe
        deer)
    fallow deer 130
    muntjac 129
    red deer 116–19, Plate IV
    reindeer 129
    roe deer 123–5, Plate IV
    sika 116, 118, 120–2

Erignathus barbatus 130
Erinaceus europaeus 43–5
Eurasian badger *see* badger
Eurasian beaver *see* beaver
Eurasian otter *see* otter
European mole *see* mole
European rabbit *see* rabbit
European roe deer *see* roe deer

Felis catus 78–81
Felis silvestris 78–81
    F.s. grampia 78
    F.s. lybica 79
ferret (feral) 102–4
fox 82–4, Plate III

goat (feral) 126–8

Halichoerus grypus 110–13
hares
    Arctic hare (*see* mountain hare)
    blue hare (*see* mountain hare)
    brown hare 37–9
    common hare (*see* brown hare)

European hare (see brown hare)
mountain hare 40–2
variable hare (see mountain hare)
white hare (see mountain hare)
hedgehog 43–5

Lepus europaeus 37–0
Lepus timidus scoticus 40–2
Lutra lutra 88–91
Lynx 130
Lynx lynx 130

Martes martes 92–4
mart/marten cat see pine marten
Meles meles 85–7
mice
 house mouse 28–30
 long-tailed field mouse (see wood mouse)
 short-tailed field mouse (see field vole)
 St. Kilda house mouse 29
 wood mouse 15, 25–7, 28, Plate I
Microtus agrestis 18–20, 21
mink see American mink
mole 46–8
Muntiacus reevesii 129
muntjac 129
Mus domesticus 28–30
Mus musculus see Mus domesticus
muskrat 129
Mustela erminea 95–8, 99
Mustela furo 102–4
Mustela furo x putorius 102–4
Mustela martes see Martes martes
Mustela nivalis 99–101
Mustela putorius 102–4
Mustela vison 105–7
Myodes glareolus 15–17, 21, 25

M.g. erica 16
Myotis daubentonii 59–61, 62
Myotis nattereri 62–3
Neomys fodiens 55–7
Neovison vison see Mustela vison
Nyctalus noctula 64–5

Odobenus rosmarus 130
Ondatra zibethicus 129
Oryctolagus cuniculus 34–6
otter 88–91, Plates II, III

Pagophilus groenlandica 130
Phoca vitulina 108–10
pine marten 92–4
Pipistrellus nathusii 72
Pipistrellus pipistrellus 66–9
Pipistrellus pygmaeus 66, 68, 70–3
Plecotus auritus 74–7
polecat 102–4
polecat-ferret see ferret (feral)
Procyon lotor 129
puma 129, 130
Puma concolor 129

rabbit 34–6, Plate IV
raccoon 129
Rangifer tarandus 129
rats
 black (ship) rat 31
 brown rat (see common rat)
 common rat 31–3
 Norway rat (see common rat)
 water rat (see water vole)
Rattus norvegicus 31–3
Rattus rattus 31
red fox see fox

Sciurus carolinensis 11, 13
Sciurus vulgaris 11–13, 14
seals
    Atlantic seal (*see* grey seal)
    bearded seal 130, Plate IV
    common seal 108–10
    Greenland seal 130
    grey seal 110–13
    harbour seal (*see* common seal)
    walrus 130
ship rat *see* black rat
shrews
    common shrew 49–51, 52
    Eurasian water shrew (*see* water
        shrew)
    pygmy shrew 52–4
    water shrew 55–7
sika 116, 118, 120–2
Sorex araneus 49–51, 52
Sorex minutus 52–4
Sorex palustris 56
squirrels
    grey squirrel 11, 13
    red squirrel 11–13, 14, Plate I
stoat 95–8, 99
Sus scrofa 114–15
sweetmart *see* pine marten

Talpa europaea 46–8

Ursus meles see Meles meles

vagrants 129–30
voles
    bank vole 15–17, 21, 25
    field vole 18–20, 21
    water vole 18, 21–4, Plate I
Vulpes vulpes 82–4

walrus 130
weasel 99–101
Western European Hedgehog *see*
    hedgehog
wild boar 114–15
wild cat 78–81
wild goat *see* goat (feral)
wolf 130